WW Healthy Kitchen™

Let's eat!

Seven C3

Produced by Seven Publishing Ltd on behalf of
WW International, Inc. Published November 2020.
All rights reserved. No part of this publication
may be reproduced, stored in a retrieval system
or transmitted in any form by any means, electronic,
mechanical photocopying, recording or otherwise,
without the prior written permission of Seven
Publishing Ltd. First published in Great Britain
by Seven Publishing Ltd.

Seven Publishing Ltd
3-7 Herbal Hill
London EC1R 5EJ
seven.co.uk

10 9 8 7 6 5 4 3 2 1

ISBN: 978-1-8381473-1-0

WW PUBLISHING TEAM
Samantha Rees, Harriet Joy,
Jessica O'Shea, Chantal Edwards
With thanks to: Shelley Fletcher

FOR SEVEN PUBLISHING LTD
EDITORIAL
Content lead: Helena Lang
Editor: Christine Faughlin
Proofreader: Ward Hellewell

FOOD
Food editor: Sarah Akhurst
Recipes: Sarah Cook, Anita Janusic,
Ella Tarn, Hannah Yeadon

DESIGN & PHOTOGRAPHY
Art director: Liz Baird
Photographer: Dan Jones
Food stylist: Matthew Ford
Prop stylist: Claire Morgan

ACCOUNT MANAGEMENT
Senior account manager: Gina Cavaciuti
Group publishing director: Kirsten Price

PRODUCTION
Print lead: Liz Knipe
**Colour reproduction by F1 Colour
**Printed in the UK by Bell & Bain Ltd

Contents

6 Welcome
8 Getting started
22 Comfort
50 Fakeaways
82 On the go
106 Weekday light
138 For the weekend
174 Entertaining
206 Useful information

Welcome

What does every busy cook need? Solutions! Making healthy meals while dealing with everything a busy life throws at you isn't always easy. And here's where this book can help. Inside, you'll find enticing recipes that taste amazing and fit into your lifestyle. There are meals to make when you're in the mood for comfort food, short on SmartPoints, entertaining, at home for the weekend, on the go – or even contemplating a takeaway. We've got breakfasts, lunches and dinners plus desserts, drinks and snacks that are all designed to help you stay on track. Plus, we've included simple meal plans to show you just how easy it is to enjoy the food you love, when you want it, and still lose weight. Enjoy!

Getting started

10   Lose weight your way
12   Even more help at hand
14   Plan for success
18   Top member tips & hacks
20   About our recipes

Lose weight your way

Looking to get healthy? We know everyone's needs are different, which is why our programme offers more than one way to experience it.

When it comes to losing weight and getting healthier, what works for one person might not work for another. At WW, we have three science-backed, proven plans (see an overview of each, right) that are tailored to fit your individual needs and personal preferences. So whichever approach you take, you can feel confident you're on the right path for you.

HOW DOES IT WORK?
It starts with the SmartPoints® system, which takes complex nutritional data and boils it down to one easy-to-understand number. Here are some basics:
● Every food and drink has a SmartPoints value based on calories, saturated fat, sugar and protein.
● You get a daily SmartPoints Budget (that's personalised to you and based on your age, weight, height and gender), as well as weekly SmartPoints for added flexibility. You can spend these on any food or drink you like, and can roll over up to four unused daily SmartPoints into your weeklies.
● You keep track of your SmartPoints in the WW app. Many ingredients are ZeroPoint™ foods, which you can use without measuring or tracking – you'll find a full list of these from page 216, and in the WW app.
● All the recipes in this book have been developed to work for each of the three plans and we've included the SmartPoints values and calories for easy tracking. Check out our 'Recipes by SmartPoints value' on page 224, for an instant overview of how different dishes stack up on different plans.

MORE THAN WEIGHT LOSS
Whichever plan you're on, the WW approach is the same: balance, enjoyment and the power of healthy habits. The helpful tools you'll get from WW will not only help you to eat better, they'll also encourage you to move more, shift your mindset to an 'I've got this' way of thinking and build life-changing habits. One such tool is the WW app – turn the page to find out how this one-stop app can help you succeed in all areas on your get-healthy journey.

ONE PROGRAMME...
and three easy ways to live it

Green guides you toward a smaller list of 100+ ZeroPoint foods that form the basis of healthy eating habits, with a sizeable SmartPoints Budget to spend on other foods you love. You'll build meals and snacks around these ZeroPoint foods including fruits and veggies, and track other foods that have SmartPoints values.

Blue guides you toward a list of 200+ ZeroPoint foods that form the basis of healthy eating habits, with a moderate SmartPoints Budget that you can spend on other foods you love. You'll build meals around these ZeroPoints foods including fruits, veggies and lean proteins, and track other foods that have SmartPoints values.

Purple guides you toward a long list of 300+ ZeroPoint foods that form the basis of healthy eating habits, with a modest SmartPoints Budget that you can spend on other foods you love. You'll build meals around these ZeroPoint foods including fruits, veggies, lean proteins and whole grains, and track other foods that have SmartPoints values.

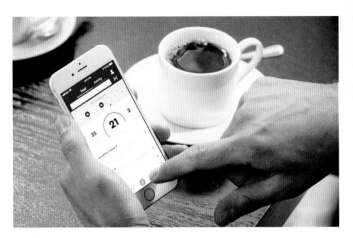

Even more help at hand

Chances are you've already downloaded the WW app for tracking SmartPoints, activity and weight-loss goals. Now you can discover a host of helpful new features...

Weight loss and wellness are about so much more than food alone – activity, mindset and sleep all play an equally important role in your progress and success. That's why *myWW+* now offers a 360° approach, with all the weight loss and wellness tools you'll ever need available at the click of a button in the new WW app.

All you need in one app
Download or update the WW app to access new and exciting features to help you stay engaged, motivated and on track.

'WHAT'S IN YOUR FRIDGE?'
On days when you've not had time to plan your meals, this tool helps you to avoid making hasty, less-healthy choices or last-minute trips to the shop. Use it to find recipe inspiration based on the ingredients you have to hand and in moments when you are likely to go off track. Tap three or four ingredients into the app and you'll be served a host of recipes making best use of those foods. You can filter results by prep and cook time, dietary preference and SmartPoints values, making 'what's for dinner?' decision-making easier than ever.

MEAL PLANNER With a plan in place, you're more likely to stay on track. This tool lets you search foods and recipes (or edit pre-populated meal plans) to customise what you eat across the week, based on your schedule, your preferences and the foods you have to hand.

PERSONALISED RECIPE RECOMMENDATIONS
Want more of what you like – and more of what works for you? You'll get suggested dishes to try based on the foods and recipes you've been tracking, and the SmartPoints you have left in your Budget.

WEEKLY WELLNESS CHECK-IN
Reflect on the previous week, set goals for the coming week and access expert tips to help you achieve your weekly goals.

PROGRESS REPORT Measuring progress by only looking at the scales doesn't always tell the full story. The Progress Report – where weight loss is at the centre, but isn't the only metric for success – lets you see and review a complete picture of your week and trends over time.

TRACKERS Use the app to easily log food, water, activity and sleep – and use the helpful barcode scanner to make choosing healthier food on the go a cinch.

ACTIVITY Moving more has never been easier! Enjoy live and on-demand equipment-free workouts you can do anytime and anywhere, via video or audio, as well as seamless integration with your wearable activity tracker.

MINDSET Get your head into 5-Minute Coaching, which offers exclusive bite-size audio content that goes beyond meditation, including science-backed mindset tools, techniques and practices to help you achieve your goals.

Plan for success

No matter how your day or week is panning out, the recipes in this book – along with clever meal planning and smart shopping – can help you stay on track.

Whatever your schedule and lifestyle, forward planning can take the stress and guesswork out of daily meal times. By setting aside an hour or so at the weekend (or whenever's convenient for you) to get ahead, you'll be better prepared for the upcoming days, and more likely to stay on track.

1 CHECK YOUR DIARY

Creating a meal plan – whether it's to cover the entire week or just the weekdays – will save you time and money. It'll also help you keep within your SmartPoints allowance and stay positive, focused and in control.

To get started, take a look at your calendar for the upcoming week and identify any hurdles, events or scenarios that could get in the way of you sticking to your healthy-eating goals. You might have a busy day at work that'll put paid to leisurely breakfast plans. Perhaps you have friends coming round at the weekend, or there's a birthday celebration on the cards. It could even be that there's a cold spell ahead that's likely to have you hankering for warming meals. Whatever's in store, jot it down.

Next, check what meals you already have in your storecupboard and freezer and decide if any will work across that week. Even just getting an idea of how many meals you'd like to cook at home and how many lunches you (or your family) might take to work or school, is an ideal way to start.

2 FIND SOME RECIPE INSPO

Once you've identified your needs for the week ahead, turn to the relevant chapters in this book to find recipe ideas for many scenarios and every meal occasion. There are new recipes to choose from, as well as tried-and-tested member favourites. You can use a combination of these and your other favourite WW recipes.

First, plan your evening meals, then fill in lunches and breakfasts. Remember to include SmartPoints values for everything, and also

factor in desserts, snacks and drinks. Here's a guide to each chapter and how they could help.

CH1: COMFORT (from P.22)
When the weather's turned, you've had a bad day, or are simply feeling a little delicate, this chapter delivers. It's packed with feel-good recipes for breakfast, lunch, dinner and dessert.

CH2: FAKEAWAYS (from P.50)
If you find yourself eyeing up the takeaway menu when Friday night comes around, go to this chapter.

How this book can help you every day

1 So you can plan easily, we've split chapters into meal occasions: breakfast, lunch and dinner, plus snacks, desserts and special occasions such as Sunday lunch.

2 Each meal occasion begins with a tried-and-tested member fave. These are the recipes that are most-tracked by members in the WW app and are a good place to start when looking for dishes your fellow members swear by.

3 Every recipe has SmartPoints for all three WW plans, so you can go for those that suit your Budget.

Find example weekly meal plans from page 208

chapter addresses all your weekend needs – from laid-back brunches and Sunday lunches to TV dinners and indulgent bakes.

CH6: ENTERTAINING (from P.174)
Life doesn't stop when you're trying to eat more healthily. There are still special occasions, family gatherings, parties, date nights and celebratory meals to enjoy. Whether you're the host or a guest contributing a dish, you'll be sorted for drinks and nibbles, barbecues, summer parties, festive gatherings, and more.

❸ HEAD TO THE SHOPS
Once you know what you're going to cook, write a shopping list based on what groceries you need and what you already have. This stops you doubling up and encourages you to use ingredients nearing their use-by date.

A list will also help you to stay focused and buy only what you need. To avoid making impulse purchases in store, write your list in aisle order so you only visit the section of the supermarket you need. If you're bombarded with offers when online shopping, click past them, or consider repeating your regular core shop with small tweaks and additions.

❹ WHEN YOU GET HOME
Identify if there's anything you can make ahead of time and keep in the fridge or freezer to streamline weekday cooking. Now's also the time to get snacks out of the way – there are lots of recipes in this book that can be made in batches and enjoyed across the week. Pack them into single-serve portions, then label with SmartPoints values for foolproof tracking.

We've turned calorific takeaways into healthier fakeaways covering everyone's favourites – from fish and chips, pizzas and burgers to Chinese stir-fries, Vietnamese noodles, Indian curries and more.

CH3: ON THE GO (from P.82)
Staying on track when you're out and about – either at work, on a picnic or taking a day trip – can be hardest of all. That's where this chapter comes in – it's made up of breakfasts, lunches and snacks that transport well, can be eaten on the go and enjoyed hot or cold.

CH4: WEEKDAY LIGHT (from P.106)
These recipes will help you on busy days when you need a quick, healthy meal that won't use up your daily Budget. There are breakfasts, dinners and snacks that come together with minimal fuss, easy-to-find ingredients and fewer SmartPoints.

CH5: FOR THE WEEKEND (from P.138)
Come Saturday, chances are you'll have more time to spend making special meals – and you'll likely have weeklies to use, too. This

Top member tips & hacks

Starting out on your WW journey? Take a tip from your fellow members and use the knowledge they've built up over the years to help you on your way.

Being a WW member is all about being part of a community – a supportive group of like-minded people who share tips to help each other out. Here's our pick of the best swaps and hacks to help you on your way to healthy-eating success.

Savvy food swaps

Swap out calorific ingredients for these low SmartPoints options – you'll never go back.

1 0% FAT GREEK YOGURT
When you want to add a thick, creamy topping or texture to a dish, use 0% fat Greek yogurt...
In baking: If a recipe contains oil or butter, replace up to half the quantity with yogurt, which will lower the fat content but keep your bake moist.
In soups: Swirl it through soup before serving in place of cream, crème fraîche or soured cream.
In sauces or dressings: Substitute mayo or soured cream for yogurt to retain a thick creamy texture.

2 SILKEN TOFU
Use this when you want a dairy-free or vegan alternative to cream, that has a neutral flavour...
In soups: Purée tofu and stir it through before serving to give soups a thick, silky texture.
In a salad: Use it in place of mayo – just purée or mash the tofu, then season with mustard, garlic and chopped fresh herbs.

In a dip: Purée tofu to make a creamy base, then stir in puréed veggies, spices and fresh herbs.

3 PURÉED VEGGIES, BEANS, PULSES & FRUIT
Try these swaps when you want to add flavour, colour and texture without extra SmartPoints...
In baking: Replace up to half the butter or oil in a recipe with puréed apples or beans.
In dips: Purée chickpeas and you have the base for houmous. Just add garlic, lemon and seasoning.
In soups: Forget cream! Cook any ZeroPoint veg (butternut squash and carrots work well) in water or stock, then purée for an easy soup that's smooth in texture.

4 VEGGIE 'CARBS'
When you want to lower the SmartPoints value of a dish that calls for rice or pasta, turn to veg…
Instead of rice or grains: Make cauliflower 'rice'. Grate 1 cauliflower, put into a microwave-safe bowl, cover with clingfilm and cook for 3 minutes until tender.
Instead of spaghetti or noodles: Spiralise courgette, butternut squash or carrot. Cook briefly, or eat raw in a slaw or noodle salad.
Instead of lasagne sheets: Slice aubergine, butternut squash or courgette lengthways, and roast for 10-15 minutes at 200°C, fan 180°C, gas mark 6. Use as you would regular lasagne sheets.

Clever kitchen hacks
Make things easier in kitchen with these ingenious tricks…

1 THE KIWI FRUIT HACK
Kiwi fruits contain a unique enzyme that rapidly breaks down protein so you can use them to tenderise meat. Mash 2 kiwi fruits in a bowl with 3 tbsp lemon juice, 3 crushed garlic cloves and 1 tbsp Dijon mustard. Season with pepper, spread over steaks and set aside for no longer than 20 minutes to tenderise. Scrape it off and cook the steaks right away. A trick for removing the fuzzy skin easily is to cut off the ends then slide a spoon under the skin and around the flesh. It'll pop out in one go.

2 THE COOKING SPRAY HACK
Mist measuring spoons and cups with calorie controlled cooking spray before measuring out sticky ingredients, such as honey, maple syrup and peanut butter – they'll slide right off.

3 THE WW WRAP HACK
WW wraps are great for sandwiches, but members use them for all kinds of things. Make chips for dips by cutting them into triangles, misting with cooking spray and baking in a hot oven. Or, use them to line a quiche instead of pastry. For more ideas, search 'WW Wraps' in the WW app.

4 THE BUTTERNUT HACK
Get zero waste from this zero hero by leaving the edible skin on when roasting (it will soften and caramelise in the oven) and saving the seeds. Pull off any stringy bits, give them a rinse, then boil in water for 10 minutes. Drain, blot dry, season with salt and bake in a hot oven until crisp. Use them to garnish soups and add crunch to salads, or eat them as a snack.

5 THE PASTA HACK
Use fresh lasagne sheets – on their own or snipped into thick ribbons – to make a pasta dish look restaurant-quality. Fold long single sheets or ribbons over on the plate and spoon ingredients and sauce in between each layer.

About our recipes

Our cookbooks are packed with healthy recipes you'll want to make time and time again.

Our philosophy is simple: to offer recipes that are nutritious as well as delicious. Our recipes are designed to encourage a healthier pattern of eating with lots of ZeroPoint foods and lower SmartPoints value ingredients to make the most of your Budget. Here's how to better understand our recipes and the ingredients that go into them.

Ingredients

EGGS We use medium eggs, unless otherwise stated. Pregnant women, the elderly and children should avoid recipes with eggs which are raw or not fully cooked if not produced under the British Lion code of practice.

FRUIT AND VEGETABLES Recipes use medium-size fruit and veg, unless otherwise stated.

LOW-FAT SPREAD When a recipe uses a low-fat spread, we mean a spread with a fat content of no more than 39 per cent.

REDUCED-FAT SOFT CHEESE Where a recipe uses medium-fat soft cheese, we mean a cheese with 30 per cent less fat than its full-fat equivalent; where a recipe uses low-fat soft cheese, we mean a soft cheese with 5 per cent fat.

Prep and cook instructions

PREP AND COOK TIMES These are approximate and meant to be guidelines only. Prep time includes all steps up to and following the main cooking time(s). Stated cook times may vary according to your oven.

MICROWAVES If we've used a microwave, the timings are for an 850-watt microwave oven.

Dietary requirements

VEGETARIAN RECIPES Recipes displaying a vegetarian symbol include non-meat ingredients, but may also contain processed products that aren't always vegetarian, such as pesto. If you're a vegetarian, ensure you use vegetarian varieties and check the ingredients labels. Where we reference vegetarian Italian-style hard cheese in vegetarian recipes, we mean a cheese that's similar to Parmesan (which is not vegetarian) but is suitable for vegetarians. For more info and guidance, visit www.vegsoc.org

'Our recipes are designed to encourage a healthier pattern of eating'

VEGAN RECIPES Recipes with a vegan symbol include no products made from or with the aid of animals or animal products. If you are vegan, ensure you use vegan varieties of processed ingredients (such as pesto) and check product labels to ensure ingredients have never been tested on animals. For more info and guidance, visit www.vegansociety.com

GLUTEN-FREE RECIPES Recipes that are labelled as gluten free include ingredients that naturally do not contain gluten, but they may also contain processed products, such as sauces, stock cubes and spice mixes. If so, ensure that those products do not include any gluten-containing ingredients (wheat, barley or rye) – these will be highlighted in the ingredients list on the product label. Manufacturers may also indicate if there's a chance their product has been contaminated with gluten during manufacturing. For more information and guidance on gluten-free products, visit www.coeliac.org.uk

NUT-FREE RECIPES Recipes displaying a nut free symbol include ingredients that do not contain nuts and/or certain seeds, but may include ingredients produced in facilities that also handle nut products. If you have a nut allergy, check ingredients labels for more information.

DAIRY-FREE RECIPES Recipes displaying a dairy free symbol include ingredients that naturally do not contain dairy, but may include ingredients produced in facilities that also handle dairy products. If you have a dairy allergy, check ingredients labels for more information.

SmartPoints calculations

SmartPoints values for all of the recipes in this book are calculated using the values for generic foods, not brands (except where stated). Tracking using branded items may affect the recorded SmartPoints.

WHEN YOU SEE THESE SYMBOLS:

0 0 0

Tells you the SmartPoints value
per serving for each plan
Note: Recipes conform to the
icon designations, but tip and
serving suggestions may not.

Indicates a recipe is gluten free

Indicates a recipe is vegetarian

Indicates a recipe is vegan

Indicates a recipe is nut free

Indicates a recipe is dairy free

Comfort

BREAKFAST
24   Baked oat waffles
26   Bloody Mary omelette
      Caramelised banana porridge
27   Breakfast rolls

LUNCH
28   Cheese & gherkin toastie
30   Turkey & leek bake
      Celeriac & smoked haddock gratin
31   Keralan chicken curry soup

DINNER
32   Chicken & mushroom stroganoff
34   Balsamic-glazed sausages with
      roasted garlic mash
36   Fish pie potato skins
38   Pork cassoulet
40   Pulled mushroom chilli with
      baked potato mash
42   Roast chicken dinner traybake
44   Oven-baked pumpkin & porcini risotto

DESSERT
46   Baked rice pudding
48   Frying pan peach crumble
      Roasted apples with cinder toffee
49   Apple & blackberry sponge puddings

MEMBERS' FAVOURITE

Baked oat waffles

serves 4   **prep time 10 minutes**   **cook time 35 minutes**

   195 kcal
per serving

Crisp and golden on the outside, sweet and chewy on the inside – no wonder WW members have been baking these comforting waffles in droves!

100g porridge oats

1 teaspoon baking powder

¼ teaspoon salt

½ teaspoon ground cinnamon

125ml semi-skimmed milk

2 bananas, mashed

Calorie controlled cooking spray

100g 0% fat natural Greek yogurt, to serve

100g blueberries, to serve

2 teaspoons clear honey, to serve

1 Preheat the oven to 180°C, fan 160°C, gas mark 4. In a bowl, combine the oats, baking powder, salt and cinnamon. Make a well in the middle of the mixture then pour in the milk, add the bananas and whisk until smooth and combined.

2 Put a 4-waffle silicone mould onto a baking tray and mist the mould with cooking spray. Spoon the oat mixture into the moulds and level the surface with the back of a spoon. Bake for 35 minutes, until cooked through and crisp around the edges.

3 Leave to cool in the mould for a few minutes before carefully turning out onto plates. Serve the waffles topped with the yogurt and blueberries, and drizzled with the honey.

Change it up

Combine 2 tablespoons PBfit powdered peanut butter with 1½ tablespoons water, then whisk this into the batter along with 20g raisins. Serve the waffles topped with sliced banana. The recipe will no longer be nut free.

Cook's tip

To make the recipe vegan, use unsweetenend oat milk instead of dairy milk and serve with soya yogurt and agave syrup instead of dairy yogurt and honey. The SmartPoints will remain the same.

Bloody Mary omelette

**serves 2   prep time 5 minutes
cook time 15 minutes**

      228 kcal per serving

Mist a nonstick frying pan with **calorie controlled cooking spray** and cook ½ chopped **red onion** over a medium heat for 6-8 minutes until soft. Add 1 small crushed **garlic** clove and cook for 1 minute, then stir in 200g halved **cherry tomatoes** and ¼ teaspoon **Tabasco sauce**. Season, then transfer to a plate and set aside. Whisk 4 large **eggs**, 50ml **semi-skimmed milk** and ½ tablespoon **creamed horseradish** together in a bowl and season well. Mist the pan with more cooking spray and pour in the egg mixture. Allow the eggs to set over the bottom of the pan, swirling to make sure the base is covered. Cook for 5 minutes until just set, then spoon the tomato mixture over one side of the omelette and fold the other side over. Remove from the pan and cut in half. Serve the omelette halves topped with a pinch of **celery salt** and ½ tablespoon chopped **fresh chives**.

Caramelised banana porridge

serves 4   prep time 5 minutes   cook time 5 minutes

      279 kcal per serving

Put 120g **porridge oats**, 600ml **unsweetened almond milk** and 300ml water into a pan over a medium heat. Bring to a simmer, then cook, stirring often, for 3-4 minutes until thick. Stir in ½ teaspoon **ground cinnamon** and 2 tablespoons **agave syrup**, then remove from the heat. Mist a nonstick frying pan with **calorie controlled cooking spray** and set over a medium heat. Cook 4 thickly sliced **bananas** for 1-2 minutes on each side until golden, then add 2 tablespoons agave syrup and allow to bubble and thicken before removing from the heat. Serve the porridge topped with the bananas and a pinch of ground cinnamon.

Breakfast rolls

serves 4   **prep time 5 minutes**   **cook time 35 minutes**

7   **5**   **5**   275 kcal per roll

Preheat the oven to 190°C, fan 170°C, gas mark 5. Cut the tops off 4 x 80g **soft wholemeal rolls** and remove and discard 15g of filling from each roll to make a cavity. Press the base of the rolls down, then put the rolls and their tops on a baking tray and mist with **calorie controlled cooking spray**. Bake for 7-8 minutes until just crisp, then set aside. Meanwhile, mist a nonstick frying pan with cooking spray and fry 200g sliced **chestnut mushrooms** over a medium heat for 4-5 minutes. Add 1 crushed **garlic** clove and cook for 1 minute. Add 80g **young leaf spinach** and stir until wilted, then season and remove from the heat. Line the cavities of the rolls with 4 x 35g thick **ham** slices, then divide the mushrooms and spinach between each. Return the rolls to the baking tray (setting aside the roll tops), then crack an **egg** into each one. Bake for 20 minutes until the whites have set but the yolks are runny. Serve with the toasted roll tops on the side.

MEMBERS' FAVOURITE

Cheese & gherkin toastie

makes 4   prep time 10 minutes   cook time 10 minutes

   237 kcal
per toastie

Tucking into a toasted cheese sandwich is one of life's great pleasures, and this meltingly good version is the one members turn to over and over again.

50g low-fat soft cheese

2 small shallots, finely diced

4 teaspoons wholegrain mustard

1 small pickled gherkin, drained and finely chopped, plus 4 extra gherkins, sliced, to serve

8 x 35g slices white farmhouse bread

85g WW Reduced Fat Grated Mature Cheese

Calorie controlled cooking spray

1   In a small bowl, combine the soft cheese, shallots, mustard and chopped gherkin, then season to taste.

2   Spread the mixture over each of the 8 slices of bread. Scatter the grated cheese over 4 of the bread slices then sandwich with the remaining bread, soft-cheese-side down.

3   Mist a large nonstick frying pan with cooking spray then set over a medium heat. Cook the sandwiches for 2-3 minutes on each side until the bread is lightly toasted and the cheese has melted – you may need to do this in batches. Serve with the extra sliced gherkins on the side.

Change it up

Instead of shallots, use 8-12 drained and chopped silverskin pickled onions. The SmartPoints will remain the same.

Turkey & leek bake

serves 4   prep time 10 minutes   cook time 45 minutes

   417 kcal per serving

Preheat the oven to 200°C, fan 180°C, gas mark 6. Put 4 x 125g **skinless turkey breast fillets** onto a baking tray, season and mist with **calorie controlled cooking spray**. Bake for 20 minutes, then shred. Meanwhile, mist a nonstick frying pan with cooking spray and fry 3 sliced **leeks** over a medium heat for 6-8 minutes until soft, then transfer to a plate. Add 3 chopped **smoked bacon medallions** to the pan and fry for 3-4 minutes, then add to the plate of leeks. Melt 1½ tablespoons **low-fat spread** in the pan, then stir in 1½ tablespoons **plain flour** and cook, stirring, for 1-2 minutes. Gradually add 400ml **semi-skimmed milk**, stirring constantly. Continue stirring over a medium heat until the sauce is thick enough to coat the back of a spoon. Remove from the heat, then stir in 1 tablespoon **wholegrain mustard** and 50g **WW Reduced Fat Grated Mature Cheese** until melted. Stir in the turkey, leeks and bacon then tip into a baking dish. Mix 150g **sourdough** chunks with ½ tablespoon chopped **fresh tarragon** and 1 teaspoon **olive oil**. Scatter over the top along with 2 tablespoons grated **Parmesan**. Bake for 20-25 minutes until golden.

Celeriac & smoked haddock gratin

serves 4   prep time 10 minutes
cook time 50 minutes

    202 kcal per serving

Preheat the oven to 200°C, fan 180°C, gas mark 6. Put 120g chopped **kale** into a colander set in the sink and pour over a full kettle of boiling water. Leave to wilt, then refresh under cold running water. Squeeze excess liquid out of the kale and set aside. Layer 600g peeled and thinly sliced **celeriac** in a 20cm x 30cm baking dish and top with the kale. Combine 300ml **chicken stock** (made with 1 stock cube) and 200g **low-fat soft cheese**, stir in a pinch of **ground nutmeg** and season. Pour over the veg and cover with kitchen foil. Bake for 30 minutes. Remove the foil and put 4 x 120g **skinless smoked haddock fillets** on top of the veg. Cover again with the foil and bake for 20 minutes. Let rest for 15-20 minutes, then scatter over ½ tablespoon chopped **fresh chives** and serve with a **green salad** on the side.

Keralan chicken curry soup

serves 4   **prep time 10 minutes**   **cook time 15 minutes**

10 **9** **7**   734 kcal per serving

Mist a large pan with **calorie controlled cooking spray** and fry 1 chopped **onion** over a medium heat for 6-8 minutes until soft. Add 2 crushed **garlic** cloves, 1 tablespoon grated **fresh ginger**, ½ chopped **green chilli**, 2 teaspoons **mild curry powder**, 1 teaspoon **fennel seeds** and 1 **cinnamon stick**, then cook for 1 minute. Pour in 400ml **reduced-fat coconut milk**, 700ml **chicken stock** (made with 1 stock cube) and bring to a simmer, then add 300g diced **potato** and cook for 5 minutes until the potato is tender. Remove and discard the cinnamon stick, then use a stick blender to blitz the soup until smooth. Stir in 200g cooked and shredded **skinless chicken breast fillet**, 100g chopped **kale** and a 250g pouch **microwave brown rice**. Simmer for 1-2 minutes, until the kale has wilted then serve garnished with **fresh coriander** and extra green chilli.

MEMBERS' FAVOURITE

Chicken & mushroom stroganoff

serves 4   prep time 10 minutes   cook time 25 minutes

 490 kcal per serving

Who wouldn't love this lighter take on the Russian classic: tender chicken and plump mushrooms simmered in a creamy sauce, served with fluffy rice and sautéed spinach.

240g brown rice

5 teaspoons olive oil

500g skinless chicken breast fillets, thinly sliced

1 onion, finely sliced

2 garlic cloves, crushed

200g chestnut mushrooms, sliced

100g baby button mushrooms

2 tablespoons plain flour

1 teaspoon paprika

250ml beef stock, made with ½ stock cube

1 tablespoon Worcestershire sauce

4 tablespoons reduced-fat soured cream

2 tablespoons chopped fresh flat-leaf parsley, plus extra to serve

2 tablespoons chopped fresh dill, plus extra to serve

250g young leaf spinach

Change it up

Make it meat-free by omitting the chicken and using 600g mixed mushrooms. Swap the beef stock cube for a veggie one, and leave out the Worcestershire sauce.

1   Bring a large pan of water to the boil, add the rice and cook to pack instructions. Drain and set aside to keep warm.

2   Meanwhile, heat 2 teaspoons of the oil in a deep nonstick frying pan over a medium-high heat. Stir-fry the chicken for 5 minutes, or until browned all over. Remove from the pan and transfer to a plate.

3   Reduce the heat to medium and add another 2 teaspoons of oil to the pan. Cook the onion, stirring, for 5 minutes or until softened. Add the garlic and mushrooms and cook, stirring, for 5 minutes or until the mushrooms are golden and tender.

4   Add the flour and paprika and cook, stirring, for 1 minute, then add the stock and Worcestershire sauce and bring to the boil. Return the chicken to the pan, reduce the heat and simmer, uncovered, for 5-7 minutes or until the sauce has thickened slightly and the chicken is cooked through. Stir in the soured cream, parsley and dill and cook for another 1 minute.

5   Meanwhile, heat the remaining 1 teaspoon oil in a large nonstick frying pan over a high heat. Cook the spinach, stirring, for 1-2 minutes or until just wilted, then remove from the heat.

6   Serve the stroganoff with the rice and spinach, garnished with the extra parsley and dill.

Balsamic-glazed sausages with roasted garlic mash

serves 4   prep time 5 minutes   cook time 25 minutes

   432 kcal per serving

What could be more comforting than a plate of bangers and mash? Here, we've puréed hearty butter beans with roasted garlic for a low-SmartPoints alternative to potatoes.

8 reduced-fat pork sausages

3 red onions, cut into thick wedges

2 tablespoons balsamic glaze

1 tablespoon olive oil

½ tablespoon wholegrain mustard

1 whole garlic bulb

400g fine green beans, trimmed

4 x 400g tins butter beans, drained and rinsed

150ml chicken stock, made with 1 stock cube

2 tablespoons roughly chopped fresh flat-leaf parsley, plus extra to serve

1 Preheat the oven to 200°C, fan 180°C, gas mark 6. Put the sausages and onions on a large baking tray. Combine the balsamic glaze, olive oil and mustard in a small jug, then pour the glaze over the sausages and onions. Toss to coat and season well. Add the whole garlic bulb to the tray and roast for 25 minutes, turning everything halfway through.

2 Five minutes before the sausages have finished cooking, bring a pan of water to the boil. Add the green beans and cook for 5 minutes until just tender, then drain and set aside to keep warm.

3 Put the tinned beans and stock into a medium frying pan and gently heat until warmed through. When the sausages are cooked, cut the garlic bulb in half horizontally and squeeze the garlic flesh into the pan of beans and stock. Season to taste and use a stick blender to blitz to a smooth mash, then stir in the parsley. Serve the mash with the sausages, onions and green beans, garnished with the extra chopped parsley.

Fish pie potato skins

serves 4   prep time 15 minutes   cook time 1 hour 30 minutes

   387 kcal per serving

Two of the world's great comfort food classics in one! We've stuffed crisp baked potato jackets with a creamy fish pie filling, then topped them with a cheesy, fluffy mash.

4 x 200g baking potatoes

Calorie controlled cooking spray

1 leek, trimmed and finely sliced

320g pack fish pie mix (we used Sainsbury's)

150g half-fat crème fraîche

1 tablespoon wholegrain mustard

½ tablespoon chopped fresh chives

½ tablespoon finely chopped fresh flat-leaf parsley, plus extra chopped leaves to serve

40g WW Reduced Fat Grated Mature Cheese

Green salad, to serve

1   Preheat the oven to 200°C, fan 180°C, gas mark 6. Put the potatoes onto a baking tray, prick the skin with a fork and bake for 1 hour to 1 hour 15 minutes until crisp on the outside and tender throughout.

2   Meanwhile, mist a small frying pan with cooking spray and fry the leek over a medium heat for 6-7 minutes until tender. Transfer to a bowl, let cool slightly, then add the fish pie mix, crème fraîche, mustard, chives and parsley. Season well and mix to combine.

3   When the potatoes are cooked, halve each one and carefully spoon out the potato flesh into another mixing bowl, leaving a 5mm shell of potato in the skin. Transfer the skins to a baking tray and fill them with the fish mixture.

4   Add 30g of the cheese to the reserved potato flesh, then season and mash until mostly smooth. Spoon the mash over the top of the fish mixture then scatter over the remaining cheese. Bake for 20-25 minutes until golden and bubbling.

5   Scatter the extra parsley over the potatoes and serve with the green salad on the side.

Cook's tip
These are great to serve on Bonfire Night or when you have guests over for dinner – you can simply double the quantities to serve more.

Pork cassoulet

serves 4   prep time 10 minutes   cook time 35 minutes

   364 kcal per serving

This herb-rich French-style stew, made with tender pork, hearty beans, smoked bacon and chopped tomatoes, is just the ticket on a chilly evening.

Calorie controlled cooking spray

500g pork tenderloin fillet, trimmed of fat and cut into 3cm cubes

4 echalion shallots, thinly sliced

2 garlic cloves, finely chopped

4 smoked bacon medallions, roughly chopped

5 sprigs fresh thyme

1 sprig fresh rosemary

1 bay leaf

1 tablespoon tomato purée

400g tin chopped tomatoes

300ml chicken stock, made with 1 stock cube

2 x 400g tins cannellini beans, drained and rinsed

2 tablespoons roughly chopped fresh flat-leaf parsley, plus extra chopped leaves to serve

Crisp green salad leaves, to serve

1   Mist a large flameproof casserole or deep nonstick frying pan with cooking spray and set over a medium heat. Season the pork well, add to the pan and brown on all sides, then transfer to a plate and set aside – you may need to do this in batches.

2   Mist the pan with more cooking spray, then add the shallots and cook for 6-8 minutes until soft, then add the garlic and bacon and cook for another 3 minutes. Add the thyme, rosemary, bay leaf and tomato purée, and cook for another minute, then stir in the chopped tomatoes and chicken stock. Season well and bring the mixture to a low simmer for 10 minutes.

3   Return the pork to the pan and simmer for 4-5 minutes until the pork is cooked through. Add the beans and cook for another 2 minutes, then remove and discard the thyme, rosemary and bay leaf. Stir through the parsley and serve with the salad on the side, garnished with the extra parsley.

●   The cassoulet can be frozen in an airtight container for up to 1 month.

Cook's tip
Serve each portion of cassoulet with a 65g crusty brown roll. The recipe will no longer be gluten-free.

Pulled mushroom chilli with baked potato mash

serves 4   prep time 5 minutes   cook time 1 hour 15 minutes

   298 kcal
per serving

Shredding mushrooms and stirring them through a spice-packed vegan chilli is a genius way to make the most of their meaty texture and intense flavour.

4 x 200g baking potatoes

Calorie controlled cooking spray

1 red onion, finely chopped

2 garlic cloves, finely chopped

1 tablespoon ground cumin

1½ tablespoons smoked paprika

1 tablespoon ground coriander

1 tablespoon tomato purée

400g tin chopped tomatoes

300ml vegetable stock, made with 1 stock cube

600g king oyster mushrooms

400g tin green lentils, drained and rinsed

Small handful fresh coriander, chopped, plus extra leaves to serve

100g plain soya yogurt

1 Preheat the oven to 200°C, fan 180°C, gas mark 6. Put the potatoes onto a baking tray, prick the skin with a fork and bake for 1 hour to 1 hour 15 minutes until crisp on the outside and tender throughout.

2 Meanwhile, mist a large, deep frying pan or flameproof casserole with cooking spray and fry the onion over a medium heat for 7-8 minutes until soft. Add the garlic and spices, and cook for another minute. Stir in the tomato purée and cook for 1 minute, then add the tomatoes and stock. Bring the mixture to a simmer, season well and cook for 20 minutes.

3 Shred the mushroom stems and caps separately, using two forks to pull them apart. Stir both into the sauce, along with the lentils, and cook for 5 minutes. Remove from the heat and stir in the coriander.

4 Halve the baked potatoes and scoop out the flesh into a bowl. Season to taste and mash until smooth.

5 Serve the chilli and mash garnished with the extra coriander, and the soya yogurt on the side.

• The chilli can be frozen in an airtight container for up to 1 month.

Cook's tip
King oyster mushrooms have the best 'pulled' texture, but if you can't find them, simply use portobello mushrooms.

Roast chicken dinner traybake

serves 4   **prep time 15 minutes**   **cook time 40 minutes**

   567 kcal per serving

Everything you love about a classic Sunday roast – juicy chicken, crispy potatoes, stuffing balls, veg and gravy – but ready in a fraction of the time. Oh, and with a lot less washing up!

600g potatoes, cut into 3cm pieces

500g carrots, cut into 3cm pieces

Calorie controlled cooking spray

100g sage and onion stuffing mix (we used Paxo)

4 x 250g chicken legs (thigh and drumstick attached), skin removed

3 sprigs fresh thyme

2 sprigs fresh rosemary

150g frozen peas

300ml chicken stock, made with 2 stock cubes

30g plain flour

Cook's tip
Feeding a crowd? Simply double the quantities and cook in 2 roasting tins.

1   Preheat the oven to 200°C, fan 180°C, gas mark 6. Put the potatoes and carrots into a large flameproof roasting tin, season well and mist all over with cooking spray. Roast for 10 minutes.

2   Meanwhile, to make the stuffing balls, mix the stuffing mix with 250ml boiling water and set aside for 5 minutes before shaping into 8 equal balls. Add the stuffing balls, chicken and herbs to the roasting tin, then mist with more cooking spray, season again, and bake for further 20-25 minutes.

3   In a jug, combine the peas and half of the stock, then add these to the roasting tin and bake for a final 10 minutes, until the peas are cooked and the chicken is golden.

4   Remove the chicken and vegetables from the tray and set aside to keep warm while you make the gravy. Set the roasting tin over a medium heat and whisk the flour into the pan juices. Gradually whisk in the remaining stock and let bubble for 2-3 minutes, until thickened. Season to taste and strain into a jug. Serve with the chicken and veg.

Oven-baked pumpkin & porcini risotto

serves 4   prep time 10 minutes + soaking   cook time 55 minutes

   319 kcal
per serving

A simple, no-stir risotto that's exactly what's needed on nights when you want to burrow beneath a blanket on the sofa with a warming bowl of something satisfying.

30g dried porcini mushrooms

Calorie controlled cooking spray

2 echalion shallots, chopped

2 garlic cloves, finely chopped

250g Arborio rice

700g pumpkin, peeled and cut into 1cm pieces

½ tablespoon finely chopped fresh sage leaves

1 teaspoon fresh thyme leaves

900ml vegetable stock, made with 2 stock cubes

40g vegetarian Italian-style hard cheese, finely grated

1   Preheat the oven to 190°C, fan 170°C, gas mark 5. Put the dried mushrooms into a small heatproof bowl and pour over 250ml boiling water from the kettle. Cover the bowl with a plate and leave to soak for 20 minutes. Drain, reserving the liquid, and roughly chop.

2   Mist a 1.5 litre flameproof casserole or deep ovenproof frying pan with cooking spray and fry the shallots and garlic over a medium heat for 5-6 minutes until starting to soften. Stir in the rice and cook for another 2 minutes. Stir in the pumpkin and rehydrated mushrooms, along with the mushroom soaking liquid and herbs, then cook for another 1 minute.

3   Season well and pour in the vegetable stock. Stir until well combined, then transfer the casserole to the oven to bake for 35 minutes. Stir in 30g of the cheese and bake for another 5 minutes.

Cook's tip
If you can't find pumpkin, or when it isn't in season, use butternut squash instead. The SmartPoints will remain the same.

4   Serve the risotto with the remaining cheese scattered over the top.

●   The risotto can be frozen in an airtight container for up to 1 month.

MEMBERS' FAVOURITE

Baked rice pudding

serves 4   prep time 5 minutes   cook time 1 hour 15 minutes

   164 kcal per serving

Often, the simplest most traditional desserts are the hardest to beat – as this ever-popular creamy vanilla rice pud with a gloriously thick skin shows.

100g pudding rice

30g Muscovado sugar

600ml skimmed milk

Pinch of salt

½ teaspoon vanilla extract

Pinch ground nutmeg, plus extra to garnish

Pared zest of 1 orange

1 Preheat the oven to 170°C, fan 150°C, gas mark 3.

2 Tip the rice into a 1.25 litre ovenproof dish. Add the sugar, milk, salt, vanilla extract and nutmeg. Stir to dissolve the sugar.

3 Bake for 1 hour to 1 hour 15 minutes until the rice is tender and a brown skin has formed on top. Spoon into bowls and serve topped with the zest.

Change it up

For something different, omit the nutmeg in Step 2 and stir in a pinch of ground cardamom instead. The SmartPoints will remain the same.

Frying pan peach crumble

serves 4   prep time 10 minutes   cook time 5 minutes

  5   183 kcal per serving

Halve, destone then thickly slice 5 **peaches** and set aside. Heat 2 nonstick frying pans over a medium heat and put 15g **low-fat spread** into each. Crumble 40g **hard amaretti biscuits** into one of the pans, then stir in 25g **porridge oats**, 15g **light brown soft sugar** and ¼ teaspoon **ground cinnamon**. Increase the heat to medium-high and cook, stirring, for 3-4 minutes until crisp and golden. Add the peach slices, 1 **vanilla pod**, halved lengthways, and 4 tablespoons water to the other pan and cook, stirring, for 2-4 minutes until the peaches have softened. Scatter the crumble over the peaches and serve warm with a 150g pot **ready-to-serve low-fat custard** divided between the 4 portions.

Roasted apples with cinder toffee

serves 4   prep time 15 minutes + cooling cook time 50 minutes

       240 kcal per serving

To make the toffee, line a small baking tray with baking paper. Put 30g **golden caster sugar**, 2 teaspoons **golden syrup** and 1 teaspoon water in a small pan over a medium-low heat. Swirl the pan and when the sugar has melted, turn up the heat. Bubble rapidly until the caramel is dark golden, then remove from the heat and beat in ½ teaspoon **bicarbonate of soda**. The mixture will foam up and increase in volume. Scrape it onto the prepared baking tray and set aside for 1 hour to cool and set, then break into shards. Preheat the oven to 180°C, fan 160°C, gas mark 4. Core and cut 6 **apples** into wedges, then put into a 1.5-litre baking dish. Spoon over 4 tablespoons water, 1 tablespoon **lemon juice** and 1 teaspoon **clear honey**, then dot over 2 teaspoons **low-fat spread**. Add 1 teaspoon **ground cinnamon**, cover with foil and bake for 30 minutes. Remove the foil, stir and bake for another 15 minutes until soft. Serve topped with 4 x 100g scoops of **lower-calorie salted caramel ice cream** (we used Jude's) and the toffee.

Apple & blackberry sponge puddings

makes 4   prep time 20 minutes   cook time 25 minutes

    230 kcal per pudding

Preheat the oven to 180°C, fan 160°C, gas mark 4. Mist 4 mini pudding moulds with **calorie controlled cooking spray** and put them into a small roasting tin. Crush 12 **blackberries** in a small bowl, then peel, core and finely dice 1 small **apple**. Add one-quarter of the apple to the blackberries and mix to combine, then spoon the mixture into the prepared moulds. Set aside the remaining apple. Combine 100g **self-raising flour**, 20g **ground almonds** and ¾ teaspoon **baking powder** in a bowl. In a jug, whisk together

75g **fat-free natural yogurt**, 2 **eggs**, ½ teaspoon **vanilla extract**, ¼ teaspoon **almond extract**, 40g **agave syrup** and 40g **apple sauce**. Whisk the wet ingredients into the dry ingredients until you have a smooth batter, then fold in the reserved apple. Divide the batter between the moulds, then pour boiling water from the kettle into the roasting tin until it reaches halfway up the sides of the moulds. Bake for 25 minutes until risen. Run a knife around the edges of the puddings to loosen them, then turn out onto serving plates. Serve warm.

Fakeaways

52   Melt-in-the-middle burgers
54   Kung pao turkey stir-fry
       French onion hotdogs
55   Beef bulgogi noodle stir-fry
56   Shawarma chicken with
       fattoush salad
58   Indonesian-style coconut prawns
       with cauliflower rice
60   Chicken tom yum soup
62   Lettuce cup beef tacos
       with jalapeño sauce
64   Vietnamese turmeric fish
66   Greek-style pork souvlaki
       with tomato rice salad
68   Sweet chilli fish & chips traybake
70   Turkish-style lamb skewers
       with couscous
72   Teriyaki cod with soba noodle salad

VEGETARIAN
74   Speedy veggie pizza
76   'Creamy' vegetable pasanda
78   Veggie katsu rice bowl
80   Korean veggie stir-fry with crispy rice
       Portobello mushroom 'pizza'

MEMBERS' FAVOURITE
Melt-in-the-middle burgers

serves 4   prep time 15 minutes   cook time 30 minutes

   374 kcal per serving

So much more than the average cheeseburger! Bite into these juicy Mediterranean-inspired patties to reveal an oozy, melted mozzarella and sundried tomato centre.

Calorie controlled cooking spray

1 small red onion, finely diced

500g extra-lean beef mince (5% fat)

½ tablespoon dried oregano

125g light mozzarella ball, quartered

50g sundried tomatoes in oil, drained and chopped

TO SERVE

2 x 80g individual ciabatta rolls

Mixed green salad leaves

1 large tomato, thickly sliced

½ red onion, thinly sliced

Change it up
Omit the sundried tomatoes, mozzarella and oregano, and stuff each of the burger patties with 15g Stilton instead. The SmartPoints will remain the same.

1   Mist a small pan with cooking spray and fry the onion over a medium heat for 8-10 minutes until softened, then set aside to cool. Tip into a bowl and add the mince and oregano. Season well and mix to combine.

2   Divide the mixture into 4 patties, then flatten each of these out slightly. Place a quarter piece of mozzarella in the centre of each, scatter over the sundried tomatoes, then form the mince mixture carefully around the cheese to encase it fully in a burger shape.

3   Mist the patties all over with cooking spray then cook on a medium-hot barbecue plate (or in a nonstick frying pan set over a medium-high heat) for 6-8 minutes on each side until just cooked through.

4   To serve, split and toast the ciabatta, then top each half with the melt-in-the-middle burgers, salad leaves, tomato and onion. Serve with extra salad.

Kung pao turkey stir-fry

serves 4   prep time 15 minutes   cook time 15 minutes

  10 9 9   425 kcal per serving

Bring a pan of water to the boil and cook 160g **jasmine rice** to pack instructions then drain. Meanwhile, grind 2 teaspoons **Szechuan peppercorns** using a pestle and mortar. Sieve, then mix the ground pepper (you'll need ¾ teaspoon) with 1 tablespoon **cornflour** on a plate. Cut 475g **skinless turkey breast** into strips and toss in the flour mixture. To make a kung pao sauce, whisk together 1 tablespoon **cornflour**, 3 tablespoons **soy sauce**, 1 tablespoon **sherry**, 1 tablespoon **rice wine vinegar** and 2 tablespoons **clear honey** and set aside. Heat 1 tablespoon **vegetable oil** in a wok over a medium heat, stir-fry the turkey for 2-3 minutes then transfer to a plate. Add 2 sliced **garlic** cloves, 6 **dried red chillies** and 6 chopped **spring onions**, stir-fry for 1 minute, then stir in the sauce. Bring to a simmer, return the turkey to the wok and cook for 1-2 minutes. Meanwhile, mist a pan with **calorie controlled cooking spray** and stir-fry 1 sliced garlic clove and 275g shredded **Brussels sprouts** over a medium heat for 3 minutes. Season and fold through the rice. Serve with the turkey stir-fry and sliced **fresh red chilli**.

French onion hotdogs

**serves 4   prep time 10 minutes
cook time 35 minutes**

   9 9 9   401 kcal per hot dog

Preheat the oven to 190°C, fan 170°C, gas mark 5. Put 8 **reduced-fat pork sausages** on a baking tray and bake for 30 minutes, turning halfway. Meanwhile, melt 1 tablespoon **low-fat spread** in a nonstick frying pan over a low heat, add 4 sliced **onions** then season and cook, stirring occasionally, for 20 minutes until soft. Add 1 tablespoon each of **wholegrain mustard**, **Worcestershire sauce** and **balsamic vinegar** to the onions, then increase the heat and cook, stirring, for 5 minutes until the onions are caramelised. Heat the grill to high. Spoon the onions into a baking dish in 4 heaped mounds. Top each mound with 2 of the sausages and lay 1 **light Dutch cheese** slice over each. Grill for 2 minutes until the cheese has melted. Meanwhile, warm 4 x 35g **plain folded flatbreads** to pack instructions. Fill the flatbreads with the cheese-topped sausages and onions, and serve.

Beef bulgogi noodle stir-fry

serves 4   prep time 20 minutes   cook time 10 minutes

      414 kcal per serving

Bring a pan of water to the boil and cook 125g **dried wholewheat noodle nests** to pack instructions, then drain and set aside. In a bowl, combine 4 tablespoons **dark soy sauce**, 4 tablespoons **mirin**, 2 crushed **garlic** cloves, 2 teaspoons **chilli flakes**, 2 teaspoons **caster sugar** and ½ tablespoon **sesame oil**. Cut 500g **rump steak** into thin slices then add to the

marinade and stir to coat. Heat ½ teaspoon sesame oil in a nonstick wok over a high heat, then stir-fry 1 **onion**, cut into thin wedges, for 2 minutes. Add the beef and all the marinade and stir-fry for 5 minutes. Remove from the heat then add the noodles, 150g **young leaf spinach** and 1 tablespoon **toasted sesame seeds**. Toss together until the spinach has wilted, then serve.

Shawarma chicken with fattoush salad

serves 4   prep time 20 minutes   cook time 10 minutes

   374 kcal per serving

Tender marinated chicken, griddled and served with a torn pitta and watermelon salad, is far more interesting than anything you'll find at the local kebab shop.

4 x 165g skinless chicken breast fillets

FOR THE MARINADE

1 teaspoon each ground cumin, ground coriander, paprika, fennel seeds and dried oregano

¼ teaspoon ground cinnamon

Grated zest and juice of 1 lemon

2 teaspoons olive oil

FOR THE FATTOUSH SALAD

1 cucumber, halved, deseeded and thickly sliced

325g tomatoes, roughly chopped

200g radishes, trimmed and thickly sliced

200g prepared watermelon, diced

Handful fresh flat-leaf parsley, leaves picked and chopped

Small handful fresh dill, chopped

4 teaspoons extra-virgin olive oil

Grated zest and juice of 1 lemon

2 x 60g wholemeal pitta breads

1   To make the shawarma marinade, mix all the marinade ingredients together in a small bowl, then season well. Brush the mixture all over the chicken and set aside to marinate for at least 15 minutes.

2   To make the fattoush salad, put the cucumber, tomatoes, radishes, watermelon and herbs into a large bowl, then toss to combine. Whisk the oil with the lemon zest and juice, then season to taste, drizzle over the salad and set aside.

3   Set a large nonstick griddle over a medium heat and griddle the chicken for 5-10 minutes on each side until lightly charred and cooked through. Remove from the griddle and let rest while you finish the salad.

4   Split the pittas, toast until crisp, then tear into bite-size chunks. Stir through the salad and toss to combine, then serve with the chicken.

Indonesian-style coconut prawns with cauliflower rice

serves 4   **prep time 15 minutes**   **cook time 20 minutes**

   287 kcal per serving

A curry that doesn't take an age to make? Yes, please! Here, tender prawns and crunchy green veg are simmered in a spicy, coconut curry sauce and served topped with cashews.

400ml tin reduced-fat coconut milk

300g courgettes, trimmed and sliced

80g mangetout

300g raw king prawns, peeled and butterflied

2 x 300g packs prepared cauliflower rice

40g roasted cashews

Lime wedges, to serve

FOR THE CURRY PASTE

1 lemongrass stalk, trimmed, tough outer layer removed, and chopped

1 onion, roughly chopped

1 tablespoon rendang curry paste

2 teaspoons ground turmeric

1   To make the curry paste, put all the paste ingredients into a mini food processor and blitz to a smooth paste. Scrape the paste into a nonstick wok or large frying pan and cook, stirring occasionally, over a low heat for 5 minutes until fragrant.

2   Stir in the coconut milk, then put 200ml water into the tin, swirl it around and add this to the pan. Bring the mixture to the boil and cook for 10 minutes.

3   Add the courgettes and mangetout to the pan, then simmer for 4-5 minutes. Stir in the prawns and simmer for another 2 minutes, until cooked through.

4   Meanwhile, cook the cauliflower rice to pack instructions and divide between bowls. Top with the curry, scatter over the cashews and serve with the lime wedges on the side.

Chicken tom yum soup

serves 4   prep time 5 minutes   cook time 10 minutes

   177 kcal per serving

If you've never tried this hot and sour Thai broth, prepare to be blown away. It's packed with fragrant lemongrass, chilli, garlic and kaffir lime, and is ready in just 15 minutes.

1 tablespoon vegetable oil

2 lemongrass stalks, ends trimmed and discarded, and stalk bashed with a rolling pin to bruise

25g fresh ginger, thinly sliced

2 garlic cloves, bruised slightly with the back of a knife

4 kaffir lime leaves

1.4 litres chicken stock, made with 1 stock cube

4 red bird's eye chillies, chopped

1 tablespoon chilli paste

240g vine cherry tomatoes

150g oyster mushrooms

2 x 120g cooked and shredded skinless chicken breast fillets

Juice of 2 limes, plus wedges to serve

60ml fish sauce

2 teaspoons palm sugar (see cook's tip)

Handful fresh coriander leaves, to serve

1   Heat the oil in a large pan over a medium heat and cook the lemongrass, ginger and garlic for 30 seconds or until fragrant.

2   Add the kaffir lime leaves and stock, increase the heat to medium-high and bring the mixture to the boil. Add the chillies and chilli paste and simmer for 5 minutes until fragrant. Add the tomatoes and mushrooms and simmer for 5 minutes or until tender.

3   Stir in the shredded chicken, lime juice, fish sauce and palm sugar. Stir until the sugar is dissolved, then ladle into bowls and garnish with the coriander leaves. Serve with the lime wedges on the side.

Cook's tip

Palm sugar is used in lots of Thai recipes and is available to buy in larger supermarkets. If you can't get hold of any, use brown sugar instead. The SmartPoints will be the same.

Lettuce cup beef tacos with jalapeño sauce

serves 4   prep time 30 minutes   cook time 15 minutes

   331 kcal per serving

These spicy chipotle beef tacos, topped with punchy salsa and a genius jalapeño sauce, will more than hit the spot when you next fancy a Mexican meal.

300g tomatoes, diced

2 shallots, halved and sliced

Small handful fresh coriander, leaves and stalks separated, stalks finely chopped

2 tablespoons tomato ketchup

1 tablespoon red wine vinegar

1 teaspoon chipotle paste

Calorie controlled cooking spray

500g extra-lean beef mince (5% fat)

2 teaspoons garlic salt

2 teaspoons sweet smoked paprika

2 teaspoons ground cumin

1 teaspoon mild chilli powder

2 tablespoons tomato purée

400g tin black beans, drained and rinsed

16 large lettuce leaves

FOR THE JALAPEÑO SAUCE

150g half-fat crème fraîche

1 teaspoon agave syrup

Grated zest and juice of 1 lime, plus wedges to serve

15g green jalapeño slices in brine, drained

1   To make the jalapeño sauce, put all the sauce ingredients into a small food processor and blitz until smooth. Season to taste and set aside.

2   Put the tomatoes, shallots and coriander stalks in a bowl. Mix together the ketchup, red wine vinegar and chipotle paste until well combined, then add to the bowl and toss to combine. Season and set aside.

3   Mist a nonstick frying pan with cooking spray and set over a medium heat. Add the beef mince and cook for 5 minutes until browned. Stir in the garlic salt, paprika, cumin and chilli powder, cook for 30 seconds, then add the tomato purée with 200ml of water. Cook, stirring, for 6-8 minutes until most of the liquid has evaporated. Stir in the black beans and coriander leaves, then season to taste.

4   Put the lettuce leaves out onto a serving board or platter and divide the beef mixture between them. Top with the tomato salsa, drizzle over the jalapeño sauce and serve with the lime wedges.

Vietnamese turmeric fish

serves 4   **prep time 10 minutes + marinating**   **cook time 15 minutes**

   325 kcal per serving

Easy, speedy and the colour of sunshine – this golden Hanoi-inspired fried fish and spicy noodle dish is super-simple yet super-delicious.

4 x 120g skinless cod fillets

4 x 50g rice vermicelli noodle nests

Calorie controlled cooking spray

6 spring onions, trimmed and cut into 5cm lengths

Handful coriander leaves, to serve

Lime wedges, to serve

FOR THE MARINADE

1 tablespoon vegetable oil

1 teaspoon ground turmeric

1 garlic clove, grated

1 teaspoon grated ginger

1 teaspoon salt

½ teaspoon caster sugar

FOR THE DRESSING

1 tablespoon fish sauce

1 tablespoon lime juice

½ tablespoon rice wine vinegar

1 teaspoon caster sugar

1 red bird's eye chilli, finely chopped

1 garlic clove, crushed

1   To make the marinade, whisk all the marinade ingredients together in a shallow dish. Add the fish, toss to coat and set aside in the fridge to marinate for 5 minutes.

2   Prepare the noodles to pack instructions, then drain and refresh under cold running water. Drain again, then set aside. To make the dressing, whisk together the fish sauce, lime juice and vinegar. Stir in the sugar until dissolved, then stir in the chilli and garlic and set aside.

3   Mist a large nonstick frying pan with cooking spray and fry the fish over a medium-high heat, turning once, for 5-6 minutes until cooked through. Remove from the pan and set aside. Mist the pan with more cooking spray and add a splash of water to deglaze the pan. Add the spring onions and stir-fry for 1-2 minutes, until slightly charred and coated in the turmeric juices.

4   Toss the noodles with the dressing and most of the coriander and divide between plates. Top with the fish, spring onions and remaining coriander, then serve with the lime wedges on the side.

Greek-style pork souvlaki with tomato rice salad

serves 4   **prep time 20 minutes**   **cook time 25 minutes**

   478 kcal per serving

Conjure up sunny days on Greek islands with griddled lemon-and-oregano pork, an olive and tomato rice salad and a generous spoonful of refreshing tzatziki.

4 x 150g pork loin medallions

1 lemon, zest grated, then cut into wedges

2 teaspoons dried oregano

¼ teaspoon ground black pepper

Calorie controlled cooking spray

FOR THE TOMATO RICE SALAD

125g long grain rice

375g cherry tomatoes, halved

3 sundried tomatoes from a jar, plus 1 tablespoon of the oil

2 tablespoons red wine vinegar

1 teaspoon dried oregano

1 red onion, diced

400g tin chickpeas, drained and rinsed

40g pitted black olives, chopped

FOR THE TZATZIKI

150g 0% fat natural Greek yogurt

¼ cucumber, deseeded and grated

1 garlic clove, crushed

1 teaspoon dried dill

1   Put the pork on a plate. In a small bowl, mix together the lemon zest, oregano, black pepper and some salt. Sprinkle the seasoning all over the pork and set aside.

2   To make the tomato rice salad, cook the rice to pack instructions, then drain and set aside in a serving bowl. Put 75g of the cherry tomatoes in a mini food processor along with the sundried tomatoes and their oil, the vinegar and oregano. Blitz to a smooth dressing then add to the rice along with the remaining cherry tomatoes and the red onion, chickpeas and olives. Stir until well combined.

3   Heat a nonstick griddle pan to high and mist the pork all over with cooking spray. Griddle for 2-3 minutes on each side until cooked through. Set aside to rest for 2 minutes while you make the tzatziki, then cut into thick strips.

4   For the tzatziki, combine the yogurt, cucumber garlic and half of the dill in a small bowl, then season to taste and scatter over the remaining dill.

5   Serve the rice salad topped with the pork and tzatziki. Drizzle over any juices from the griddle pan, and serve with the lemon wedges on the side.

Sweet chilli fish & chips traybake

serves 4   **prep time 10 minutes**   **cook time 35 minutes**

    379 kcal per serving

Friday-night fish suppers have never looked – or tasted – as good. Even better, it's all cooked in the one roasting tin, so you won't even have to worry about the washing up.

600g sweet potatoes, cut into chunky chips

1 tablespoon vegetable oil

1 tablespoon sesame seeds

5 tablespoons light sweet chilli sauce

Grated zest of 1 lime plus the juice of ½ lime

300g Tenderstem broccoli

4 x 125g skinless basa fillets

1 spring onion, trimmed and thinly sliced on the diagonal, to serve

2 tablespoons chopped fresh coriander, to serve

Cook's tip
Don't worry about peeling the sweet potato chips – the edible skin gets softer when roasting, and helps the chips hold their shape when they soften and turn caramelised.

1   Preheat the oven to 200°C, fan 180°C, gas mark 6. Line a large baking tray with baking paper. Put the sweet potatoes into a large bowl, drizzle over the oil and sprinkle over the sesame seeds. Season well then toss together and spread out onto the prepared tray. Roast for 20 minutes, then turn them over and cook for another 5 minutes.

2   Meanwhile, whisk together the chilli sauce, lime zest and juice in a small jug, then season and set aside.

3   Bring a medium pan of water to the boil and add the broccoli. When it comes back to the boil, leave it for 30 seconds, then immediately drain it.

4   Push the sweet potato chips to one end of the baking tray and arrange the basa fillets and the blanched broccoli at the other end. Brush the fish with the sweet chilli mixture, and season the broccoli.

5   Bake everything together for 10 minutes until the fish is cooked through and the broccoli is tender. Serve garnished with the spring onions and coriander.

Turkish-style lamb skewers with couscous

serves 4   **prep time 35 minutes + marinating**   **cook time 10 minutes**

   412 kcal per serving

Fans of Middle Eastern cuisine are sure to love this easy dish of pomegranate-marinated lamb skewers, grilled and served with a colourful couscous salad.

500g lean lamb leg steaks, cut into 2cm pieces

2 teaspoons cumin seeds

1 teaspoon ground coriander

1 teaspoon sumac, plus a little extra to serve

2 tablespoons pomegranate molasses

FOR THE SALAD

125g wholewheat couscous

200ml hot vegetable stock, made with ½ stock cube

Juice of 2 lemons

1 red onion, diced

1 yellow pepper, deseeded and diced

½ cucumber, diced

Small handful fresh mint leaves, roughly chopped or torn

125g pomegranate seeds (optional)

1   Put the lamb into a bowl and add the cumin seeds, coriander, sumac, pomegranate molasses and some freshly ground black pepper. Toss everything together to combine, then set aside to marinate for 1 hour (or cover and put in the fridge to marinate overnight).

2   To make the salad, put the couscous into a large mixing bowl and pour over the hot stock. Cover and set aside for 10 minutes, until all the liquid is fully absorbed. Fluff up the couscous grains with a fork, then stir through half the lemon juice and the onion, pepper, cucumber, mint and pomegranate seeds, if using. Add the rest of the lemon juice to taste, and sprinkle over the extra sumac.

3   Heat the grill to high. Thread the lamb onto 4 skewers and grill for 5-8 minutes, turning occasionally, until the lamb is cooked to your liking. Serve the skewers with the couscous.

Teriyaki cod with soba noodle salad

serves 4   prep time 15 minutes   cook time 20 minutes

   370 kcal per serving

If you're looking for an easy Japanese main to make at home, look no further. We've paired sticky sweet teriyaki glazed cod with a tasty ginger and sesame dressed noodle salad.

4 x 120g skinless cod fillets

40ml thick teriyaki sauce

150g frozen peas

250g broccoli, cut into florets

1½ teaspoons sesame oil

150g 100% buckwheat soba noodles

4 spring onions, trimmed and thinly sliced on the diagonal

Handful fresh coriander, leaves roughly chopped

1 tablespoon black sesame seeds

FOR THE SALAD DRESSING

2 teaspoons sesame oil

3 tablespoons rice wine vinegar

1 x 20g ball stem ginger, drained and roughly chopped

1   Put the cod fillets into a shallow dish, pour over the teriyaki sauce, cover, and set aside for 10 minutes to marinate at room temperature.

2   Meanwhile, bring a small pan of water to the boil, add the peas and cook for 3 minutes, then drain and set aside.

3   To make the salad dressing, put all the dressing ingredients into a mini food processor and blitz until smooth. Season to taste and set aside.

4   Preheat the oven to 200°C, fan 180°C, gas mark 6. Put the cod on a baking tray and brush over any of the teriyaki sauce still in the dish. Toss the broccoli florets with the sesame oil in a mixing bowl, then season and add to the tray with the cod. Roast for 12-15 minutes until the cod is cooked through.

5   Cook the noodles to pack instructions, then drain, rinse under cold running water and drain again. Drizzle over the dressing and add the peas, spring onions and coriander. Add the roasted broccoli and toss everything together, then scatter over the sesame seeds. Serve the noodles with the roasted cod.

Cook's tip

For a bit of added heat, whisk ¼ teaspoon wasabi paste into the dressing before drizzling it over the noodle salad. The SmartPoints will stay the same.

MEMBERS' FAVOURITE
Speedy veggie pizza

makes 4   prep time 5 minutes   cook time 10 minutes

   325 kcal
per serving

Homemade pizza beats shop-bought any day of the week. This popular recipe is on the table in 15 minutes flat – faster than any takeaway service!

1 tablespoon rapeseed oil

4 tablespoons tomato purée

1 tablespoon dried mixed herbs

4 WW Wholemeal Wraps

2 red peppers, deseeded and cut into strips

2 yellow peppers, deseeded and cut into strips

120g mushrooms, sliced

4 spring onions, trimmed and finely sliced

120g WW Reduced Fat Grated Mature Cheese

40g vegetarian Italian-style hard cheese, grated

4 tablespoons chopped fresh basil (optional)

1 Preheat the oven to 180°C, fan 160°C, gas mark 4. Line 2 baking trays with baking paper.

2 To make a pizza sauce, mix the oil, tomato purée and dried herbs with 1 tablespoon water, then season.

3 Put the wraps on the prepared baking trays, spread with the sauce and top with the peppers, mushrooms and spring onions. Scatter over the WW Reduced Fat Grated Mature Cheese and bake for 10 minutes.

4 Scatter over the Italian-style hard cheese and basil, if using, then serve.

Change it up
Omit the tomato sauce and spread 4 sachets WW Barbecue Sauce, mixed with 2 teaspoons rapeseed oil, over the base of the pizza before adding the toppings. The SmartPoints will remain the same.

'Creamy' vegetable pasanda

serves 4   prep time 15 minutes   cook time 25 minutes

   250 kcal per serving

On nights when nothing but an Indian-style curry will do, turn to this deliciously mild version. It's packed with veg in a creamy-style sauce that you can mop up with naan bread.

Calorie controlled cooking spray

1 onion, diced

2 garlic cloves, crushed

2 teaspoons grated fresh ginger

6 cardamom pods, squashed with a rolling pin

1 tablespoon mild curry powder

1 teaspoon ground turmeric

1 tablespoon cornflour

500ml unsweetened almond drink

150ml vegetable stock, made with ½ stock cube

350g carrots, cut into large pieces

350g cauliflower florets

200g green beans, trimmed

20g flaked almonds

20g desiccated coconut

2 x 300g packs cauliflower rice

75g plain soya yogurt

Lime wedges, to serve

Cook's tip
Serve the curry with 4 WW mini naan breads. The recipe will longer be vegan, dairy free or gluten free.

1   Mist a large nonstick frying pan with cooking spray and fry the onion over a medium heat for 6-8 minutes until soft. Stir in the garlic, ginger and cardamom pods and cook for 2 minutes, then add the curry powder and turmeric and cook for 30 seconds.

2   In a small jug, mix the cornflour with enough of the almond drink to make a smooth paste, then add this to the pan, along with the remaining almond drink and the stock. Simmer gently for 10 minutes.

3   While the sauce is cooking, bring a large pan of water to the boil. Add the carrots and cook for 1 minute, then add the cauliflower and cook for another 1 minute, and then add the beans and cook for 2 minutes. Drain the veg well, then stir them into the sauce. Cover with a lid and cook for 5 minutes.

4   Crumble the almonds into a separate frying pan to break them up a bit. Add the coconut and toast together over a medium heat until golden and fragrant. Meanwhile, cook the cauliflower rice to pack instructions.

5   Remove the curry from the heat and stir in the yogurt. Season to taste, scatter over the toasted almonds and coconut and serve with the cauliflower rice and lime wedges on the side.

•   The curry can be frozen without the soya yogurt in an airtight container for up to 1 month.

Veggie katsu rice bowl

serves 4   prep time 20 minutes   cook time 25 minutes

   264 kcal per serving

A clever spin on the classic Japanese curry – roasted aubergine tossed with rice, lentils, kale and a homemade curry sauce, topped with pickled shallots and a crunchy crumb.

1 tablespoon vegetable oil

1 tablespoon lemon juice

1½ teaspoons ground turmeric

2 aubergines, sliced into 3cm-thick rounds

20g panko breadcrumbs

300ml chilled unsweetened coconut drink

1 tablespoon medium curry powder

125g shredded kale

2 x 250g pouches microwave brown basmati rice & quinoa

Fresh coriander sprigs, to serve

FOR THE PICKLED SHALLOTS

2 echalion shallots, thinly sliced into rounds

2 tablespoons rice wine vinegar

¼ teaspoon caster sugar

1   Preheat the oven to 200°C, fan 180°C, gas mark 6. To make the pickled shallots, mix the shallots with the vinegar, sugar and a pinch of salt in a small bowl, then set aside to pickle, stirring occasionally, while you make the rest of the dish.

2   In a small jug, whisk together the oil, lemon juice and 1 teaspoon of the turmeric. Put the aubergines into a large roasting tin, drizzle over the turmeric oil and toss to coat. Roast for 20-25 minutes until the aubergine is charred at the edges and tender. Transfer to a bowl and set aside.

3   Put the panko breadcrumbs on a small baking tray and put in the oven alongside the aubergines for the last 2-3 minutes of roasting time – keep an eye on them to ensure they don't burn.

4   Put the coconut drink into a large pan and whisk in the remaining turmeric and the curry powder. Cover with a lid and simmer gently for 5 minutes. Add the kale to the pan with the sauce, cover and leave it on the heat for 30 seconds to start wilting, then remove from the heat.

5   Meanwhile, heat the rice and quinoa to pack instructions. Stir into the pan of sauce and kale, along with half of the roasted aubergines. Season to taste.

6   Divide between bowls, top with the remaining aubergine, scatter over the toasted breadcrumbs and coriander sprigs and serve with the pickled shallots.

Portobello mushroom 'pizza'

**serves 4   prep time 10 minutes
cook time 15 minutes**

  200 kcal
per serving

Pierce a 100g bag **young leaf spinach** then microwave on High for 1 minute until wilted. Squeeze out as much water as you can, then chop the spinach and set aside to cool. Stir in 125g **ricotta**, 15g grated **light mozzarella**, 15g grated **half-fat Cheddar,** 1 tablespoon chopped **fresh basil** and a pinch of **ground nutmeg**. Remove the stalks from 4 large **portobello mushrooms,** then chop these and stir them into the spinach mixture. Season well. Heat the grill to high and line a grill pan with kitchen foil. Put the mushrooms, stalk-side down, on the prepared pan and mist with **calorie controlled cooking spray**. Grill for 6 minutes, then turn and spoon over the spinach mixture. Combine 200g **passata** with 1 teaspoon each of **garlic granules**, **dried oregano**, **red wine vinegar** and **agave syrup,** then season and spoon over the spinach mixture. Top with 15g grated light mozzarella and 15g grated half-fat Cheddar and grill for 8-10 minutes. Serve with 4 **reduced-fat garlic and herb baguette slices.**

Korean veggie stir-fry with crispy rice

serves 4   prep time 15 minutes   cook time 15 minutes

  392 kcal per serving

Cook 240g **jasmine rice** to pack instructions, then drain and set aside. In a jug, whisk together 2 crushed **garlic** cloves, 3 tablespoons **ketchup**, 1½ tablespoons **light soy sauce**, 1 tablespoon **dark soy sauce**, 1 tablespoon **maple syrup**, 2 teaspoons **chilli paste** and 2 tablespoons water. Mist a nonstick wok with **calorie controlled cooking spray** and stir-fry 2 sliced **onions** over a medium heat for 2 minutes. Add 3 diced **mixed peppers**, 150g **baby button mushrooms** and 150g **baby corn**, increase the heat to high and stir-fry for 1-2 minutes. Stir in the sauce, then reduce the heat and simmer for 2-4 minutes. To make the crispy rice, heat ½ tablespoon **vegetable oil** in a nonstick frying pan and fry 6 sliced **spring onions** over a medium heat for 1-2 minutes. Remove from the pan, stir into the cold rice and season. Heat ½ tablespoon vegetable oil in the pan, add the rice mixture and press it flat. Cook for 5-10 minutes until crisp underneath. Use a fork to break it up, then divide between bowls, top with the stir-fry and serve garnished with extra sliced spring onions.

On the go

BREAKFAST

84 Homemade granola

86 Banana mocha frappe

Beetroot & blueberry smoothie

87 Roasted strawberry & almond overnight oats

LUNCH

88 Turkey, apple & smoked Cheddar wraps

90 Hot smoked salmon Caesar salad

Italian-style pesto salad

91 Sesame chicken salad

92 Spring vegetable spanakopita

94 Pea & Parma ham quiche

96 Pesto chicken pasta salad

98 Roasted cauliflower, ham & mustard frittata

SNACKS

100 Carrot cake flapjacks

102 PBJ granola cups

Pumpkin & chia seed bites

103 Raspberry blondies

104 Apple pie cookies

Hot & spicy pulse pot

105 Spring onion & bacon mini muffins

MEMBERS' FAVOURITE

Homemade granola

serves 15   prep time 10 minutes   cook time 25 minutes

   182 kcal
per serving

Spend a little time whipping up a batch of this ever-popular granola and you'll be rewarded with no less than 15 breakfasts that are good to go when you are.

275g porridge oats

70g flaked almonds

½ teaspoon salt

100g clear honey

60ml vegetable oil

1 teaspoon vanilla extract

4 tablespoons pumpkin seeds

50g puffed rice cereal (we used Rice Krispies)

1 Preheat the oven to 170°C, fan 150°C, gas mark 3½ and line 2 baking trays with baking paper.

2 In a large bowl, combine the oats, almonds and salt. In a separate smaller bowl, combine the honey, oil and vanilla extract, then fold this through the oat mixture until the dry ingredients are completely coated. Spoon the mixture onto the prepared baking trays and spread out in an even layer.

3 Bake for 15 minutes, then stir in the pumpkin seeds. Return to the oven and bake for another 10 minutes, or until golden.

4 Set aside to cool completely, then stir through the puffed rice cereal.

Cook's tip

Serve 40g granola with 40g 0% fat natural Greek yogurt and the fresh fruit of your choice. The recipe will no longer be dairy free.

• The granola will keep in an airtight container for up to 2 weeks.

Banana mocha frappe

makes 2   prep time 5 minutes

      81 kcal per frappe

Stir 1 teaspoon **cocoa powder** in 80ml freshly brewed **espresso coffee** until dissolved. Put 8 ice cubes into a blender and pour over the mocha espresso. Let cool then add 1 large roughly chopped **frozen banana** and 160ml **skimmed oat milk**. Blend until smooth and creamy, then pour into glasses or travel mugs to serve.

Cook's tip: The mixture will settle and separate slightly so if you're taking it out and about, make sure you give it a good stir or shake before drinking.

Beetroot & blueberry smoothie

makes 2   prep time 5 minutes

      59 kcal per smoothie

Put 100g **cooked beetroot** (not in vinegar), 100g **frozen blueberries**, 80ml **freshly squeezed orange juice** and 30g **0% fat natural Greek yogurt** into a blender and blitz until smooth and combined. Pour into 2 small glasses and serve.

Roasted strawberry & almond overnight oats

serves 4   prep time 5 minutes + overnight soaking   cook time 20 minutes

6 **6** **3**   218 kcal per serving

The night before serving, roast the strawberries. Preheat the oven to 200°C, fan 180°C, gas mark 6, and line a baking tray with baking paper. Hull and halve 300g **strawberries** and toss with 1 tablespoon **agave syrup** and the zest of 1 **lemon**. Put on the prepared tray and roast for 20 minutes. Remove from the oven, transfer to a bowl and crush slightly. In a bowl, combine 120g **porridge oats**, 320ml **skimmed oat milk** and 1 teaspoon **vanilla extract**, then swirl through the roasted berries. Cover and chill in the fridge overnight. The next morning, loosen the oats with a splash of water, divide between bowls and top with 100g sliced strawberries and 20g toasted **flaked almonds**.

MEMBERS' FAVOURITE

Turkey, apple & smoked Cheddar wraps

makes 2   prep time 15 minutes

   272 kcal
per serving

Sandwiches can be as simple or complicated as you like, and this quick and easy wrap is the one that's making WW members smile at lunchtime.

2 WW Wholemeal Wraps

1 tablespoon wholegrain mustard

4 large lettuce leaves

1 stick celery, thinly sliced

1 apple, halved, cored and cut into thin matchsticks

4 x 20g slices cooked turkey breast

20g slice smoked Cheddar (we used Applewood), cut into 4 thin strips

1 Put the wraps on a board and spread the mustard evenly down the centre of each.

2 Top with the lettuce, celery, apple, turkey and cheese, then roll and wrap to serve.

Change it up

Omit the mustard and make a Waldorf salad-style yogurt dressing to spread over the wrap instead. Mix ¼ teaspoon English mustard with 40g 0% fat natural Greek yogurt, 1 chopped sprig of tarragon and a squeeze of lemon juice. Season to taste and spread over the wrap before adding the remaining ingredients.

Hot smoked salmon Caesar salad

**serves 4   prep time 10 minutes
cook time 20 minutes**

   284 kcal per serving

Bring a pan of water to the boil, add 4 **eggs** and boil for 1 minute. Turn off the heat, cover with a lid and set aside for 9 minutes. Drain, let cool then peel and set aside. Meanwhile, preheat the oven to 200°C, fan 180°C, gas mark 6. Mist a baking tray with **calorie controlled cooking spray** and then mist 4 x 20g slices **ciabatta**. Rub all over with the cut sides of 1 halved **garlic** clove, then season and top with 10g grated **Parmesan**. Bake for 15-20 minutes, then cut into croutons. To make a dressing, whisk together 100g **0% fat natural Greek yogurt**, 2 tablespoons **lighter than light mayonnaise**, 2 teaspoons **olive oil**, 1 teaspoon **Worcestershire sauce**, 1 teaspoon **Dijon mustard**, and the juice of ½ **lemon**. Crush ½ garlic clove and stir into the dressing along with 2 chopped **anchovy fillets** and 2 teaspoons **capers**, then season and set aside. Chop 2 **Baby Gem lettuces** and flake 2 x 90g **hot smoked salmon fillets**. To assemble the salad, toss together the lettuce, salmon and dressing, then scatter over the croutons and top with the egg halves.

Italian-style pesto salad

**serves 4   prep time 15 minutes
cook time 40 minutes**

   246 kcal per serving

Preheat the oven to 200°C, fan 180°C, gas mark 6. Line 1 large baking tray with baking paper. Cut 1 **aubergine** (you'll need 400g) and 1 **courgette** (you'll need 300g) into 2cm cubes, then add to the trays along with 2 diced **red peppers**. Spoon over 30g **reduced-fat red pesto**, mist with **calorie controlled cooking spray**, then season and toss together. Roast for 35-40 minutes. Thickly slice 150g **ciabatta** and rub with the cut sides of 1 halved **garlic** clove, then cut into 2cm pieces. Mist with cooking spray, put onto a baking tray and bake alongside the veg for the final 10 minutes. Remove the croutons and veg from the oven and set aside to cool. In a bowl, toss the roasted veg with 30g reduced-fat red pesto and 100g **young leaf spinach**. Tear 125g **light mozzarella** into pieces, then add to the salad. Season and store in airtight containers in the fridge until ready to eat, scattering over the croutons just before serving.

Sesame chicken salad

serves 4   **prep time 15 minutes**
cook time 30 minutes

3   **2**   **2**   227 kcal per serving

Put 3 **fresh coriander** sprigs, 1 teaspoon **peppercorns**, 10g sliced **ginger**, 2 chopped **spring onions** and 1 **star anise** into a large pan. Fill with cold water and bring to the boil. Add 4 x 165g **skinless chicken breast fillets**, bring back to the boil then reduce to a low simmer. Cover and poach for 20 minutes, until cooked through. Discard the poaching liquid and shred the chicken. Meanwhile, halve 2 large **cucumbers** lengthways, then put onto a board, cut-side down. Use a rolling pin to smash the cucumbers along the length until they split. Discard the seeds, then chop the cucumber and put into a colander set over a bowl. Sprinkle over 1 teaspoon **salt** and mix well, then cover and refrigerate for 30 minutes. To make a dressing, combine 1½ tablespoons each **rice wine vinegar** and **soy sauce**, 1½ teaspoons each **toasted sesame oil** and **caster sugar**, and 1 small crushed **garlic** clove in a bowl. To assemble the salad, shake the colander to drain excess liquid from the cucumber, then put in a bowl. Toss with the chicken, 2 sliced spring onions and the dressing, then scatter over 2 teaspoons **toasted sesame seeds** and some coriander leaves and serve.

Spring vegetable spanakopita

serves 4   prep time 10 minutes   cook time 50 minutes

 376 kcal per serving

How to make spanakopita – the classic Greek filo pie of spinach, feta and herbs – even tastier than it already is? Simply add more veg!

Calorie controlled cooking spray

2 leeks, trimmed and thinly sliced

200g asparagus, trimmed and cut into 3cm lengths

2 garlic cloves, finely chopped

240g young leaf spinach

150g frozen peas

Large handful fresh dill, chopped

Small handful fresh mint, chopped

100g light feta cheese, crumbled

2 large eggs, lightly beaten

7 sheets filo pastry

1   Preheat the oven to 200°C, fan 180°C, gas mark 6. Mist a large nonstick frying pan with cooking spray and fry the leeks and asparagus over a medium heat for 7-8 minutes until tender. Add the garlic and cook for another minute. Remove from the heat and set aside.

2   Put the spinach and peas into a colander set over the sink and pour over a full kettle of boiling water. Leave for 2 minutes, then use the back of a spoon to press out as much liquid from the spinach as possible.

3   Put all of the vegetables into a mixing bowl, season, then stir in the herbs, feta and eggs. Set aside.

4   Mist an 18cm loose-bottomed cake tin with cooking spray, then arrange a sheet of filo so it covers the base and sides of the tin. Mist again and repeat with 4 more sheets of filo, making sure to cover the whole surface area of the tin. Spoon in the veggie mixture, then scrunch the remaining filo over the top and mist with cooking spray. Fold any overhang of filo over the edge of the tin, then bake for 35-40 minutes until the pastry is crisp and golden – loosely cover the tin with kitchen foil if the pastry starts to brown too much before the cooking time is up.

5   Let the pie cool in the tin slightly, before cutting into quarters to serve.

•   The spanakopita can be frozen in an airtight container for up to 1 month. Defrost overnight in the fridge.

Cook's tip

This is the perfect dish for when you're on the go and is just as delicious served hot or cold. Keep it in the tin, covered with a reusable lid or beeswax cover. That way you can serve it straight from the tin, or else warm it in a low oven if you want to.

Pea & Parma ham quiche

serves 4   prep time 10 minutes   cook time 50 minutes

    310 kcal per serving

What's a picnic or outdoor gathering without quiche? This one makes clever use of WW Wraps instead of pastry to help keep the SmartPoints low.

Calorie controlled cooking spray

3 WW White Wraps

3 shallots, finely chopped

250g frozen peas

4 slices Parma ham, chopped

4 large eggs, lightly beaten

150ml chicken stock, made with ½ stock cube

70g WW Reduced Fat Grated Mature Cheese

2 tablespoons finely chopped fresh flat-leaf parsley, plus extra chopped leaves to serve

1 tablespoon finely chopped fresh mint

Mixed salad leaves, to serve

1 Preheat the oven to 200°C, fan 180°C, gas mark 6. Mist the wraps with cooking spray, then put one of the wraps, misted-side down, in an 18cm loose-bottomed cake tin. Cut the other wraps in half and arrange them to line the base and sides of the tin, making sure to cover all gaps. Set aside.

2 Mist a nonstick frying pan with cooking spray, and cook the shallots over a medium heat for 5-6 minutes until soft, then add the peas and cook for another 2 minutes. Transfer to a mixing bowl. Stir in the Parma ham, eggs, chicken stock, half of the grated cheese and all of the herbs until well combined, then season well.

3 Scatter the remaining cheese over the base of the lined tin, then pour in the egg mixture. Bake the quiche for 40-45 minutes until set and lightly golden. Leave to rest in the tin for 10 minutes, then carefully remove and scatter over the extra parsley. Cut into quarters and serve with the mixed salad leaves.

Cook's tip
The quiche is cooked when the filling has a slight wobble when you pull it out of the oven.

Pesto chicken pasta salad

serves 4   prep time 10 minutes + resting   cook time 15 minutes

 450 kcal
per serving

Everyone needs a good pasta salad recipe up their sleeve and this mayo-free version really shines. Served warm or cold, in a lunchbox or as part of a buffet, it's sure to win you over.

4 x 165g skinless chicken breast fillets

2 tablespoons reduced-fat green pesto

Calorie controlled cooking spray

160g orzo pasta

200g purple sprouting broccoli, trimmed and larger florets cut into small pieces

12 cherry tomatoes, halved

Handful fresh basil leaves, roughly torn

Handful fresh mint leaves, roughly chopped

20g Parmesan, shaved, to serve

25g toasted pine nuts, to serve

FOR THE DRESSING

Grated zest and juice of 1 lemon

1 tablespoon olive oil

1 Put the chicken between 2 pieces of clingfilm and bash with a rolling pin to flatten slightly. Brush half the pesto over one side of each chicken fillet.

2 Mist a large nonstick frying pan with cooking spray, heat to medium-high and add the chicken, pesto-side down. Brush the remaining pesto over the top of each fillet and cook, turning once, for 15 minutes, or until cooked through and golden. Remove from the pan and set aside to rest for 5 minutes before cutting into thick strips.

3 Meanwhile, bring a pan of water to the boil, add the orzo and cook to pack instructions. When the pasta has 4-5 minutes of cooking time to go, add the broccoli to the pan. Drain well and set the orzo and broccoli aside in a large bowl.

4 Add the pesto chicken, tomatoes and herbs to the bowl and toss until well combined. Just before serving, make the dressing. Whisk together the lemon zest, lemon juice and oil, then season to taste. Drizzle the dressing over the salad and serve topped with the Parmesan and pine nuts.

Roasted cauliflower, ham & mustard frittata

serves 4   **prep time 10 minutes**   **cook time 1 hour**

   251 kcal
per serving

Roasting cauliflower gives it a unique nutty flavour and crunchy texture – bake it with ham and mustard into a frittata-like savoury cake and you'll have the perfect picnic fare.

1 large cauliflower, trimmed and cut into small florets (you'll need 500g)

Calorie controlled cooking spray

240g young leaf spinach

120g ham, roughly torn

6 large eggs

1 tablespoon Dijon mustard

320g mixed green veg (we used green beans, asparagus tips and Tenderstem broccoli)

Grated zest and juice of 1 lemon

1   Preheat the oven to 200°C, fan 180°C, gas mark 6. Put the cauliflower onto a baking tray, mist with cooking spray and season well. Roast for 15-20 minutes until tender and lightly golden.

2   Put the spinach into a colander set over the sink and pour over a full kettle of boiling water. Leave for 2 minutes to wilt, then let cool slightly before pressing as much liquid out as possible and roughly chopping.

3   Mix the chopped spinach, roasted cauliflower and ham together in a mixing bowl. Whisk the eggs and mustard together in a separate bowl, then add this to the ham mixture and stir to combine.

4   Mist the base and sides of a 20cm cake tin with cooking spray, line with baking paper and put onto a baking tray. Pour in the egg mixture and bake for 40 minutes until set and golden, then let cool for 5 minutes before removing from the tin.

5   Meanwhile, cook the mixed green vegetables in a pan of boiling water for 3 minutes until tender but still al dente, then drain and refresh under cold running water. Set aside to chill, toss with the lemon zest and juice and season to taste. Serve the cauliflower cake with the zesty greens.

MEMBERS' FAVOURITE

Carrot cake flapjacks

makes 20   **prep time 15 minutes**   **cook time 30 minutes**

     94 kcal per flapjack

These moist, oaty bars are already winning over members up and down the country. To make them even more memorable, we've added a cream cheese glaze for no extra SmartPoints.

100g low-fat spread

3 tablespoons golden syrup

225g porridge oats

2 eggs, lightly beaten

2 carrots, grated

40g sultanas

Grated zest of 1 orange

1½ teaspoons mixed spice

FOR THE CREAM CHEESE GLAZE

50g medium-fat soft cheese, brought to room temperature

20g icing sugar

¼ teaspoon vanilla extract

3 teaspoons skimmed milk

1 Preheat the oven to 180°C, fan 160°C, gas mark 4. Melt the low-fat spread in a large pan over a low heat. Brush a little of the melted spread over the base and sides of a 30cm x 20cm Swiss roll tin, then line the base with baking paper.

2 Stir the golden syrup into the melted spread, then add the remaining flapjack ingredients to the pan. Stir until everything is well combined.

3 Tip the mixture into the prepared tin and smooth the surface with a spatula. Bake for 25-30 minutes until golden. Cool in the tin for 30 minutes to firm up, then remove from the tray to cool completely.

4 To make the cream cheese glaze, whisk the cheese in a small bowl until fluffy, then whisk in the icing sugar and vanilla extract. Stir in the milk, until the mixture reaches a drizzling consistency, then drizzle it over the flapjacks before cutting into 20 bars.

Cook's tip

Boost the carrot cake flavours even further by stirring 50g toasted chopped walnuts through the mixture before baking. The recipe will no longer be nut free.

PBJ granola cups

**makes 20   prep time 25 minutes
cook time 15 minutes**

    67 kcal per granola cup

Preheat the oven to 160°C, fan 140°C, gas mark 2½.
Combine 125g **porridge oats** and 25g **plain flour** in a
bowl. Melt 75g **clear honey**, 20g **low-fat spread** and
60g **smooth peanut butter** in a small pan set over
a medium-low heat. Stir to combine, then remove
from the heat and stir in the oat and flour mixture.
Spoon into a 24-hole silicone mini muffin mould
– you'll have enough mixture to fill 20 of the holes.
Use your thumb to press the mixture firmly into
each hole and make a dip in the centre to form a
cup. Bake for 12 minutes. Using a teaspoon, divide
75g reduced-sugar strawberry jam between the
cups then bake for another 3-4 minutes until the jam
melts and the cups turn golden. Let cool completely
before removing from the mould. The granola cups
will keep in an airtight container for up to 5 days.

Pumpkin & chia seed bites

makes 18   prep time 20 minutes

    56 kcal per bite

Put 115g **porridge oats**, 125g **tinned pumpkin
purée**, 85g pitted **Medjool dates**, ½ teaspoon
vanilla extract, 1 teaspoon **ground cinnamon**,
¼ teaspoon **ground ginger**, 20g **chia seeds** and
1 tablespoon **maple syrup** into a food processor.
Blitz until the mixture is finely chopped and starts
to come together into a ball. Add 25g **pumpkin
seeds** and pulse them into the mixture for a
couple of seconds – don't overdo it as you want
them to retain a bit of their crunchy texture. Use
your hands to roll the mixture into 18 x 20g balls,
then store between layers of baking paper in an
airtight container. The bites will keep in an airtight
container in the fridge for up to 5 days, or frozen
for up to 1 month.

Raspberry blondies

**makes 16   prep time 15 minutes
cook time 30 minutes**

5   4   4   117 kcal per blondie

Preheat the oven to 180°C, fan 160°C, gas mark 4.
Grease a 20cm x 30cm baking tin with 1 teaspoon
low-fat spread, and line the base and sides with
baking paper. Melt 75g **white chocolate** in the
microwave then set aside. Drain and rinse a 400g tin
cannellini beans, then put into a food processor with
2 **eggs** and blitz until smooth. In a mixing bowl, use
an electric whisk to beat 50g **low-fat spread** and
75g **coconut sugar** until pale and fluffy. Beat in 1 egg
and 2 teaspoons **vanilla extract**, then fold in 100g
plain flour and 1 teaspoon **baking powder**, followed
by the bean mixture and melted white chocolate.
Spread the batter into the prepared tin, then scatter
over 125g **raspberries** and 25g chopped white
chocolate. Bake for 25-30 minutes until a skewer
inserted into the centre comes out clean. Set aside
to cool. Dust with ½ teaspoon **icing sugar**, then cut
into 16 pieces. The blondies will keep in an airtight
container for up to 2 days, or frozen for up to 1 month.

Apple pie cookies

**makes 14   prep time 25 minutes
cook time 15 minutes**

      98 kcal per cookie

Preheat the oven to 180°C, fan 160°C, gas mark 4 and line 2 baking trays with baking paper. Melt 50g **low-fat spread** and 25g **golden syrup** together in a pan. Remove from the heat and stir in 50g **light brown soft sugar**, then leave to cool for 2 minutes before stirring in 1 teaspoon **vanilla extract** and 1 beaten egg. Add 100g **plain wholemeal flour**, 100g **porridge oats**, ½ teaspoon **bicarbonate of soda**, 1¼ teaspoons **ground cinnamon**, 1 teaspoon **mixed spice** and the grated zest of 1 **lemon**, then stir to combine. Peel, core and cut 1 **apple** into 1cm cubes, then fold into the mixture. Spoon 14 scoops of the cookie mixture onto the prepared trays, spacing them well apart, then flatten slightly with wet fingers. Bake for 10 minutes until golden. Cool for 5 minutes on the tray, then transfer to a wire rack to cool completely. Mix 15g **icing sugar** with enough cold water to reach a drizzling consistency. Drizzle over the cooled cookies, then leave to set before serving. The cookies can be kept in an airtight container for up to 3 days, or frozen for up to 1 month.

Hot & spicy pulse pot

**serves 6   prep time 5 minutes
cook time 25 minutes**

      101 kcal per serving

Preheat the oven to 190°C, fan 170°C, gas mark 5. Drain, rinse then pat dry a 400g tin **chickpeas**. Tip the chickpeas onto a baking tray, drizzle over 1 teaspoon **olive oil**, then scatter over ½ teaspoon each **cumin seeds** and **sweet smoked paprika**. Toss to coat, then spread out on the tray. Roast for 15 minutes. Add 20g each **pumpkin seeds** and **sunflower seeds**, 2 teaspoons **maple syrup**, ½ teaspoon **chilli flakes** and ½ teaspoon **cayenne pepper** to the tray, then season well. Toss together then roast for 10 minutes until the chickpeas are golden. Cool on the tray, then divide into portions and transfer to airtight containers or bags. Serve on its own as a savoury snack, or scatter over a salad for extra flavour and crunch. The mixture will keep in an airtight container for up to 5 days.

Spring onion & bacon mini muffins

makes 24 **prep time 15 minutes** **cook time 20 minutes**

2 **2** **2** 53 kcal per mini muffin

Preheat the oven to 200°C, fan 180°C, gas mark 6. Mist a nonstick frying pan with **calorie controlled cooking spray** and fry 3 diced **smoked streaky bacon rashers** over a medium heat for 5-8 minutes until crisp. Transfer to a plate lined with kitchen paper and set aside. In a bowl, mix together 75g **self-raising flour**, 50g **wholemeal plain flour**, 1 teaspoon **baking powder**, 20g grated **Parmesan** and ¼ teaspoon **salt**. In a jug, whisk together 2 **eggs**, 50ml **skimmed milk** and 3 tablespoons **sunflower oil**. Make a well in the centre of the dry ingredients, pour in the egg mixture and stir until smooth and combined, then fold through the bacon and 3 sliced **spring onions**. Mist a 24-hole nonstick mini muffin tin with cooking spray, then spoon the mixture into the holes. Scatter over 5g grated Parmesan, then bake for 10-12 minutes until risen and golden. The muffins will keep in an airtight container in the fridge for up to 2 days or frozen for up to 1 month.

Weekday light

BREAKFAST

108 Scrambled eggs with mushrooms & smoked trout

110 Banana, berry & chocolate cereal pots

Chia & coconut Bircher muesli with blueberry compote

111 Peach & almond baked oats

DINNER

112 Steak & pepper quesadillas

114 Spring chicken traybake

116 Vegan agedashi tofu

118 Tamarind-glazed salmon with crunchy naked slaw

120 Tapenade tuna salad

122 Spanish chicken & butter bean bravas

124 Veggie cannelloni

Pasta with anchovies & capers

125 Warm courgette pasta salad

126 Harissa steak salad

128 Sticky spiced chicken & butternut squash traybake

130 Spiced turkey mujadarra

SNACKS

132 Spicy roasted chickpeas

134 Seed crackers with artichoke dip

136 Choc-chip flapjack bites

Frozen yogurt-coated blueberries

137 Frozen chocolate & raspberry bark

MEMBERS' FAVOURITE

Scrambled eggs with mushrooms & smoked trout

serves 4   prep time 5 minutes   cook time 10 minutes

   260 kcal
per serving

Rise and dine on a top-rated cooked breakfast that's low in SmartPoints and on the table in just 15 minutes – the perfect way to start the day.

8 large flat mushrooms

Calorie controlled cooking spray

8 eggs

4 tablespoons chopped fresh chives

2 small garlic cloves, crushed

120ml skimmed milk

250g hot smoked trout, flaked

1 tablespoon chopped fresh dill, to serve

1 lemon, cut into wedges, to serve

Change it up

Drain and roughly chop 4 tablespoons capers, then stir these through the egg mixture before cooking. Scatter a few more over the finished dish, just before serving. The SmartPoints will remain the same.

1   Heat the grill to medium-high and line a large grill pan with kitchen foil. Put the mushrooms, stem-side down, on the prepared pan and mist with cooking spray. Cook under the grill for 6 minutes, then turn and mist with more cooking spray. Season well and grill for a final 3-4 minutes.

2   Meanwhile, whisk together the eggs, chives, garlic and milk, then season well. Mist a large nonstick frying pan with cooking spray and set over a medium heat. Add the egg mixture and scramble for 2-3 minutes, until cooked through.

3   Divide the mushrooms between plates, top with the scrambled eggs, smoked trout and dill. Serve with the lemon wedges on the side.

Banana, berry & chocolate cereal pots

serves 4   prep time 5 minutes

      250 kcal per serving

Divide 60g **WW Spelt Cereal with Chocolate** between 4 small bowls or jars. Top each jar with 1 thickly sliced **banana** followed by 50g **0% fat natural Greek yogurt**. Scatter another 10g of WW Spelt Cereal with Chocolate into each pot, then spoon over another 50g 0% fat natural Greek yogurt and finish with **fresh berries**.

Chia & coconut Bircher muesli with blueberry compote

serves 4   prep time 10 minutes + overnight chilling cook time 10 minutes

      177 kcal per serving

Put 100g **porridge oats**, 300ml chilled **unsweetened coconut drink** (we used Alpro), 1 tablespoon **chia seeds**, 1 cored and grated **apple** and ½ teaspoon **ground cinnamon** into a bowl and mix well. Cover and chill overnight in the fridge. The next day, put 1 teaspoon **agave syrup**, 200g **blueberries** and the juice of ½ **lemon** in a small pan. Cover and cook for 5 minutes over a medium heat, until softened. Remove the lid and cook for 5 minutes until reduced and syrupy. Spoon the muesli into bowls and top with 80g **plain soya yogurt with coconut** and the blueberry compote.

Peach & almond baked oats

**serves 4   prep time 10 minutes
cook time 30 minutes**

(8) (5) (2)   279 kcal per serving

Preheat the oven to 200°C, fan 180°C, gas mark 6. Put 125g **porridge oats**, 2 tablespoons **maple syrup**, 3 beaten **eggs**, 1 teaspoon **baking powder**, 200g **0% fat natural Greek yogurt**, ½ teaspoon **almond extract** and 1 teaspoon **vanilla extract** into a bowl and stir well to combine. Tip the mixture into a 1-litre ovenproof dish and arrange 2 thickly sliced **peaches** over the top of the oat mixture, pressing each slice into the oats. Bake for 30 minutes, until golden, then serve with 240g 0% fat natural Greek yogurt.

MEMBERS' FAVOURITE DINNER

Steak & pepper quesadillas

serves 4   prep time 15 minutes   cook time 30 minutes

   361 kcal per serving

When WW members fancy a Mexican meal, pronto, they turn to this crisp tortilla sandwich filled with juicy rump steak, melted cheese, peppers, chillies and herbs.

Calorie controlled cooking spray

2 x 200g rump steaks

1 red pepper, deseeded and sliced

1 yellow pepper, deseeded and sliced

1 red onion, halved and sliced

1 garlic clove, finely chopped

½ teaspoon chilli flakes

4 WW White Wraps

135g WW Reduced Fat Grated Mature Cheese

Handful coriander leaves, plus extra leaves to serve

Mixed green salad, to serve

Lime wedges, to serve

Change it up

Add some sliced jalapeño peppers to the filling and serve the quesadillas with a fresh homemade oil-free tomato salsa on the side. The SmartPoints will stay the same.

1   Mist a large nonstick frying pan with cooking spray. Season the steaks and sear over a medium-high heat for 2 minutes on each side. Remove from the pan and set aside to rest for 10 minutes, then thickly slice.

2   Meanwhile, mist the pan with more cooking spray and stir-fry the peppers and onion over a medium-high heat for 6-8 minutes. Add the garlic and chilli flakes and cook for 1 minute. Transfer to a bowl.

3   Mist the pan with more cooking spray and add one of the wraps. Scatter over a quarter of the cheese, followed by half of the pepper mixture and half of the steak. Scatter over another quarter of the cheese and half of the coriander. Top with a second wrap, mist with more cooking spray and cook for 3-4 minutes, pressing down with a spatula. Carefully flip the quesadilla and cook on the other side for another 3-4 minutes, or until the wraps are golden and the cheese is melted. Remove from the pan then repeat to make a second quesadilla.

4   Cut the quesadillas into quarters and serve 2 quarters per person, with the salad, extra coriander and lime wedges.

Spring chicken traybake

serves 4   prep time 10 minutes   cook time 1 hour

   385 kcal per serving

What's especially great about this one-pan dish is that it's completely hands-off – once you toss all the fresh ingredients together in a roasting tin, the oven takes care of the rest.

700g Jersey Royal potatoes, halved

100g spring onions, trimmed and halved

500g asparagus, trimmed

240g mixed radishes, larger ones halved

3 garlic cloves, crushed slightly with the flat side of a knife

Small handful fresh tarragon, chopped

Juice of 1 lemon

Calorie controlled cooking spray

4 x 165g skinless chicken breast fillets, each scored 3 times

100g fat-free natural yogurt

½ teaspoon Dijon mustard

1   Preheat the oven to 190°C, fan 170°C, gas mark 5. Put the potatoes into a large roasting tin with the spring onions, asparagus, radishes, garlic and half of the tarragon and lemon juice, then mist all over with cooking spray. Season well and toss everything together. Arrange the chicken on top, mist with more cooking spray and season well. Cover with foil and bake for 30 minutes.

2   Remove the foil and cook for another 30 minutes, until the chicken is golden and cooked through and the vegetables are tender.

3   Meanwhile, mix the yogurt with the mustard and the remaining tarragon and lemon juice. Season and drizzle over the traybake just before serving.

Cook's tip

If you've only ever eaten peppery radishes raw, you'll be amazed at how much more juicy and mellow in flavour they become when roasted with nothing more than a little seasoning.

Vegan agedashi tofu

serves 4   prep time 10 minutes + soaking and draining   cook time 10 minutes

   159 kcal per serving

Looking for new ways with tofu? Our healthier take on this popular Japanese dish is pan-fried rather than deep-fried and comes together easily.

25g dried porcini mushrooms

2 x 300g packs silken tofu

20g cornflour

Calorie controlled cooking spray

2 tablespoons mirin

2 tablespoons light soy sauce

½ teaspoon sugar

4 spring onions, trimmed and shredded, to serve

10g ginger, cut into very thin matchsticks, to serve

1 small red chilli, sliced, to serve (optional)

Cook's tip

Bulk up this dish with fresh mushrooms. Fry 300g sliced chestnut mushrooms with the rehydrated porcini mushrooms in Step 3, and add both to the broth. The SmartPoints will remain the same.

1   Put the mushrooms in a medium heatproof bowl and pour over 500ml boiling water from the kettle. Cover and set aside for 30 minutes to soak. Strain the mushroom soaking liquid through a fine sieve into a small pan, pressing any excess liquid from the mushrooms using the back of a spoon. Finely slice the rehydrated mushrooms and set aside.

2   Meanwhile, drain the tofu. Wrap each block in kitchen paper and set aside to drain for 30 minutes. Cut each block into 6 equal pieces, pat dry again with kitchen paper, then dust with the cornflour and set aside.

3   Mist a nonstick frying pan with cooking spray and set over a high heat. Fry the tofu for 5-10 minutes, turning occasionally until all sides are golden – you may need to do this in batches. Remove from the pan and set aside on a plate lined with kitchen paper. Mist the pan with more cooking spray and fry the rehydrated mushrooms for 2-3 minutes until golden.

4   In a small pan, bring the mushroom soaking liquid, mirin, soy sauce, sugar and a pinch of salt to the boil. Cook for 1-2 minutes, or until the sugar has dissolved, then stir in the mushrooms.

5   To serve, divide the tofu between bowls, top with the spring onions, ginger and chilli, if using, then carefully pour the stock and mushrooms around the tofu.

Tamarind-glazed salmon with crunchy naked slaw

serves 4   prep time 10 minutes   cook time 20 minutes

   284 kcal per serving

Sour tamarind, hot chillies and oil-rich fish work brilliantly together in this quick and easy Thai-style fish supper.

1 tablespoon tomato purée

2 tablespoons tamarind paste

1 tablespoon soy sauce

½ teaspoon chilli flakes

4 x 130g skinless salmon fillets

Lime wedges, to serve

FOR THE NAKED SLAW

1 carrot, peeled into thin ribbons

350g white cabbage, shredded

Small handful fresh coriander leaves, chopped, plus extra leaves to serve

Small handful fresh mint leaves, plus extra leaves to serve

1 red chilli, deseeded and chopped

2 teaspoons finely grated ginger

4 spring onions, trimmed and finely shredded

Juice of 1 lime

1 Preheat the oven to 190°C, fan 170°C, gas mark 5. Line a baking tray with baking paper.

2 Put the tomato purée, tamarind paste, soy sauce and chilli flakes into a mixing bowl and stir to combine. Brush the mixture all over the salmon fillets, then transfer to the prepared tray. Bake for 15-20 minutes, until cooked through.

3 Meanwhile, prepare the slaw. Put the carrot, cabbage, coriander and mint in a bowl and toss together to combine. Add the chilli, ginger, spring onions and lime juice, and toss to fully coat.

4 Serve the salmon fillets and slaw topped with coriander, with the lime wedges on the side.

Cook's tip
If you have time, leave the salmon fillets to marinade in the tamarind glaze for a fuller flavour. Cover and put in the fridge for 1 hour.

Tapenade tuna salad

serves 4   **prep time 10 minutes**   **cook time 5 minutes**

   337 kcal per serving

On evenings when time isn't on your side, this speedy tuna steak supper comes into its own. All that's needed is a bit of chopping and a quick sear on the griddle.

4 x 140g tuna steaks

1 tablespoon black olive tapenade

Calorie controlled cooking spray

400g mixed tomatoes, chopped

1 cucumber, trimmed and sliced

½ red onion, thinly sliced

100g light feta, crumbled

60g pitted black olives

FOR THE DRESSING

Juice of ½ lemon

1 tablespoon olive oil

1 tablespoon red wine vinegar

1 teaspoon dried oregano

2 tablespoons fat-free natural yogurt

1   Rub the tuna all over with the tapenade. Mist a nonstick frying pan or griddle pan with cooking spray and set over a medium heat. Griddle the tuna for 1-2 minutes on each side, then remove from the heat and set aside to rest for 5 minutes while you make the salad and dressing.

2   For the dressing, whisk all the dressing ingredients together in a small jug, then season to taste.

3   Put the tomatoes, cucumber, red onion, feta and olives in a serving bowl, drizzle over the dressing and toss to combine. Serve with the tuna steaks.

Spanish chicken & butter bean bravas

serves 4   **prep time 10 minutes**   **cook time 25 minutes**

    315 kcal per serving

We've swapped potatoes for butter beans in this satisfying lower SmartPoints take on the smoky tapas favourite, then topped it with griddled paprika-spiced chicken.

Juice of 1 lemon

1 garlic clove, finely chopped

1 teaspoon smoked paprika

4 x 165g skinless chicken breast fillets

Calorie controlled cooking spray

FOR THE BUTTER BEAN BRAVAS

3 shallots, finely chopped

2 garlic cloves, finely chopped

½ teaspoon chilli flakes

1 teaspoon smoked paprika

400g tin chopped tomatoes

½ teaspoon sugar

1 tablespoon red wine or sherry vinegar

2 x 400g tins butter beans, drained and rinsed

200g fine green beans

Small handful fresh flat-leaf parsley, chopped

1 In a small jug, mix together the lemon juice, garlic and smoked paprika, then season well. Put the chicken in a bowl and mist with cooking spray, then stir in the lemon juice mixture. Cover and put in the fridge to marinate for 20 minutes.

2 Meanwhile, make the butter bean bravas. Mist a nonstick pan with cooking spray and fry the shallots and garlic over a medium heat for 2-3 minutes, until starting to soften. Add the chilli flakes and paprika, and cook for 1 minute, then add the chopped tomatoes, sugar, vinegar and butter beans. Bring to a gentle simmer and cook for 15 minutes.

3 While the beans are simmering, mist a large nonstick frying pan with cooking spray and set over a medium heat. Add the chicken and cook for 5-10 minutes on each side, or until cooked through and golden. Remove from the pan and let rest for 5 minutes, before slicing thickly.

4 Cook the green beans in a pan of boiling water for 5 minutes, then drain. Serve with the butter bean bravas and chicken, garnished with the parsley.

Veggie cannelloni

serves 4   prep time 30 minutes
cook time 45 minutes

      297 kcal per serving

Bring a pan of water to the boil and cook 100g **peas** and 250g chopped **asparagus** for 2-3 minutes. Drain and refresh under cold running water. Mist a nonstick frying pan with **calorie controlled cooking spray** and fry 300g diced **courgettes** over a high heat for 5 minutes. Add 100g sliced **spring onions** and the asparagus and peas and cook for 1 minute, then add 1 chopped **garlic** clove and a pinch of **ground nutmeg** and cook for 1 minute. Stir in 100g **ricotta** and a handful of torn **fresh basil**, then season. Preheat the oven to 200°C, fan 180°C, gas mark 6. Spoon the courgette filling into 12 x 10g **cannelloni tubes**. To make a sauce, whisk together 225g **quark**, 1 **egg**, a handful of torn fresh basil and 30g grated **vegetarian Italian-style hard cheese**, then season. Spoon a little of the sauce over the base of a medium baking dish along with any leftover filling. Lay the cannelloni on top, pour over the remaining sauce and scatter over 10g grated vegetarian Italian-style hard cheese. Bake for 30-35 minutes and serve with a **green salad**.

Pasta with anchovies & capers

serves 4   prep time 5 minutes
cook time 15 minutes

      287 kcal per serving

Bring a pan of water to the boil and cook 240g **WW Yellow Lentil Spaghetti** to pack instructions. Drain and set aside, reserving a cup of cooking water. Meanwhile, put 35g torn **gluten-free bread** into a mini food processor and blitz into breadcrumbs. Mist a nonstick frying pan with **calorie controlled cooking spray** and toast the crumbs over a high heat for 3-4 minutes, stirring, until golden. Transfer to a bowl, wipe the pan with kitchen paper and return it to the hob. Reduce the heat to medium, mist the pan with more cooking spray and fry 12 **anchovy fillets in oil**, drained and chopped, 2 chopped **garlic** cloves and 3 tablespoons chopped **capers** for 2 minutes. Stir in the grated zest and juice of 1 **lemon**, then add the cooked spaghetti with a little of the pasta cooking water and 15g finely grated **Parmesan**. Season to taste and toss well to combine. Serve topped with the breadcrumbs and 15g Parmesan shavings.

Warm courgette pasta salad

serves 4   prep time 5 minutes   cook time 25 minutes

(6) (6) (4)   199 kcal per serving

Peel 2 **courgettes** into ribbons, mist with **calorie controlled cooking spray** and season. Heat a large nonstick griddle pan to high and griddle the courgette ribbons, in batches, for 2 minutes on each side. Set aside and cut into long, thin strips. Meanwhile, bring a pan of water to the boil and cook 100g **wholewheat spaghetti** to pack instructions. Drain, reserving a cup of cooking water, and put the pasta into a serving bowl. Add the courgette, 40g **toasted pine nuts**, 40g **raisins**, the grated zest and juice of ½ **lemon**, and a little of the reserved pasta cooking water to the spaghetti. Toss together, then season and serve topped with 10g grated **vegetarian Italian-style hard cheese**.

Harissa steak salad

serves 4   prep time 15 minutes   cook time 20 minutes

   343 kcal
per serving

A spicy, substantial Moroccan-inspired dish that's equally delicious served warm for dinner or prepped ahead and assembled cold for lunch the next day.

500g new potatoes, halved

200g Tenderstem broccoli

150g fine green beans

2 tablespoons harissa paste

550g lean beef rump steak

Calorie controlled cooking spray

75g fat-free natural yogurt

Juice of ½ lemon

Handful fresh chives, chopped

80g baby leaf salad

200g roasted peppers in brine, drained and sliced

50g light feta, crumbled

1   Cook the potatoes in a large pan of boiling water for 15 minutes, then add the broccoli and green beans and cook for a further 5 minutes. Drain and set aside.

2   Meanwhile, rub all but 1 teaspoon of the harissa paste over the steaks and set aside. Mist a nonstick frying pan with cooking spray and set over a medium-high heat. Sear the steaks for 2 minutes on each side, then remove from the pan and set aside to rest for 10 minutes before slicing.

3   Mix the remaining harissa paste with the yogurt, lemon juice and half of the chives. Arrange the salad leaves, peppers, potatoes, broccoli, beans and steak on plates. Scatter over the feta and remaining chives then drizzle over the harissa yogurt and serve.

Sticky spiced chicken & butternut squash traybake

serves 4   prep time 15 minutes + marinating   cook time 1 hour

   477 kcal per serving

Butternut squash and Brussels sprouts bring colour and flavour to this simple Chinese-style chicken dinner, not to mention a boost to your 5-a-day quota.

2 tablespoons soy sauce

1 tablespoon toasted sesame oil

2 tablespoons clear honey

3 garlic cloves, finely chopped

2 teaspoons grated ginger

Juice of 1 lime

Handful fresh coriander, leaves and stalks chopped separately

4 x 165g skinless chicken breast fillets

800g butternut squash, peeled, deseeded and cut into 2cm pieces

100g spring onions, trimmed and halved

2 red chillies, deseeded and sliced

1 red pepper, deseeded and sliced

250g Brussels sprouts, trimmed

Calorie controlled cooking spray

125g wild rice

1 Preheat the oven to 220°C, fan 200°C, gas mark 7. In a non-metallic mixing bowl, combine the soy sauce, sesame oil, honey, garlic, ginger, lime juice and coriander stalks. Add the chicken and toss to coat, then cover and put in the fridge to marinate for 30 minutes while you roast the veg.

2 Put the butternut squash, spring onions, chillies, red pepper and sprouts into a large roasting tin and mist with cooking spray. Season well and bake for 30 minutes. Turn the oven down to 200°C, fan 180°C, gas mark 6. Lift the chicken from the marinade, pour any remaining marinade over the vegetables, then nestle the chicken fillets among them. Bake for another 30 minutes, until cooked through.

3 Meanwhile, bring a large pan of water to the boil, add the rice and simmer over a low heat for 25 minutes. Drain well.

4 Serve the rice topped with the chicken and vegetables. Drizzle over any juices from the roasting tin and scatter over the coriander leaves.

Spiced turkey mujadarra

serves 4   prep time 20 minutes   cook time 40 minutes

   506 kcal
per serving

Mujadarra is a popular Middle Eastern side dish of lentils and rice with herbs and caramelised onions. Served with spiced turkey mince and veg, it makes for a hearty, filling main meal.

1 onion, sliced

500g turkey breast mince

125g cherry tomatoes, sliced

100g young leaf spinach

1 garlic clove, chopped

2 teaspoons ras el hanout

10g fresh ginger, finely grated

2 green chillies, finely sliced

Handful fresh coriander, chopped

FOR THE MUJADARRA

1 tablespoon vegetable oil

2 onions, sliced

Calorie controlled cooking spray

3 garlic cloves, chopped

1 teaspoon ground cinnamon

1 tablespoons ras el hanout

150g brown rice

250g pouch ready-to-eat Puy lentils

Handful fresh coriander, chopped

Handful fresh flat-leaf parsley, chopped

1 For the mujadarra, heat the vegetable oil in a large pan over a medium heat. Add the onions, stir to coat, then reduce the heat to low and cook, covered, for 10 minutes until softened. Remove the lid, increase the heat to medium and cook, stirring, for 3-4 minutes until golden. Transfer to a bowl and set aside.

2 Mist the pan with cooking spray, add the garlic, cinnamon and ras el hanout, and cook for 1 minute. Stir in the rice along with 700ml water and bring the mixture to a gentle boil. Cover and cook for 20 minutes then remove the lid, add the lentils and continue to cook for 5 minutes, until all the water has been absorbed. Stir through the herbs, return the onions to the pan and season to taste.

3 While the mujadarra is cooking, make the spiced turkey. Mist another pan with cooking spray and set over a medium heat. Add the onion and cook for 5 minutes, stirring, until it starts to soften, then add the turkey mince and cook for another 5 minutes. Stir in the tomatoes and spinach, and cook for 2 minutes, then add the garlic, ras el hanout, ginger and chillies, and cook for 1 minute. Stir in the coriander.

4 Divide the mujadarra between plates and top with the spiced turkey.

MEMBERS' FAVOURITE

Spicy roasted chickpeas

serves 4   prep time 5 minutes   cook time 45 minutes

   76 kcal per serving

There are plenty of reasons why members turn to these crunchy, spicy chickpeas at snacktime – they're easy to make, very low in SmartPoints and utterly delicious.

400g tin chickpeas, drained and rinsed

Calorie controlled cooking spray

1 teaspoon ground cumin

1 teaspoon smoked paprika

Pinch cayenne pepper

1   Preheat the oven to 180°C, fan 160°C, gas mark 4. Pat the chickpeas dry with kitchen paper, then put into a mixing bowl. Mist with cooking spray and add the spices and a good pinch of sea salt and freshly ground black pepper. Toss to coat then spread the chickpeas out onto a small baking tray.

2   Mist the chickpeas with more cooking spray and roast for 45 minutes, shaking the tray halfway through cooking. Tip into a small bowl and serve warm.

•   The cooled chickpeas will keep in an airtight container for up to 1 week, but they'll soften with time.

Change it up
Mist the same quantity of chickpeas with cooking spray, then season well with sea salt. Roast in the oven for 30 minutes, then stir through the zest and juice of 1 lime and 2 teaspoons freshly ground black pepper. Return to the oven and bake for a final 15 minutes. The SmartPoints will stay the same.

Seed crackers with artichoke dip

serves 8   prep time 20 minutes   cook time 15 minutes

   182 kcal
per serving

Making a batch of homemade crackers is easier than you might think – and well worth it. These are extra crunchy and delicious thanks to a combo of five different seeds.

60g mixed seeds (we used sunflower, pumpkin, sesame and linseed)

20g chia seeds

125g plain flour, plus an extra 10g for dusting

1 tablespoon olive oil

1 teaspoon clear honey

FOR THE ARTICHOKE DIP

400g tin artichoke hearts in water, drained

1 shallot, roughly chopped

1 garlic clove, roughly chopped

100g fat-free natural yogurt

1 sprig fresh rosemary, leaves stripped and finely chopped

50g vegetarian Italian-style hard cheese, finely grated

75g quark

Pinch chilli flakes

1   Preheat the oven to 220°C, fan 200°C, gas mark 7 and line 2 baking sheets with baking paper. Put the mixed seeds, chia seeds and flour into a bowl. Mix the olive oil, honey and 75ml tepid water together in a small jug, then stir this into the seed and flour mixture until it all comes together. Knead to a dough.

2   On a surface lightly dusted with the extra flour, roll out the dough until it's about 3mm thick. Cut into 32 evenly sized pieces, then put them onto the prepared baking sheets in a single layer. Bake for 12-15 minutes, until brown at the edges. Set aside to cool and crisp up.

3   Meanwhile, to make the dip, put the artichokes, shallot and garlic into a food processor and blitz until smooth. Add the yogurt, rosemary, grated cheese and quark, then pulse until combined. Transfer to a bowl, scatter over the chilli and serve with the crackers.

●   The crackers will keep in an airtight container for up to 1 week.

Choc-chip flapjack bites

**makes 20 prep time 10 minutes
cook time 20 minutes**

  75 kcal per flapjack bite

Preheat the oven to 190°C, fan 170°C, gas mark 5.
Line a baking sheet with baking paper. Melt 100g
low-fat spread and 50g **light brown soft sugar**
in a pan set over a low heat. Stir in 50g chopped
pitted **dates** and transfer the mixture to a food
processor. Blitz until smooth. Scrape into a bowl,
then stir in 150g **porridge oats** and 50g **dark
chocolate chips** until combined. Using a teaspoon,
place small spoonfuls of the mixture onto the
prepared baking tray and cook for 12-15 minutes,
until golden brown. Remove from the oven and
leave to cool. The flapjack bites will keep in
an airtight container for up to 5 days.

Frozen yogurt-coated blueberries

serves 4 prep time 10 minutes + freezing

   45 kcal per serving

Put 100g **0% fat natural Greek yogurt** and
1 tablespoon **maple syrup** in a bowl and stir
well to combine. Add 200g **blueberries** and
stir to coat. Line a baking tray with baking paper.
Using a fork, transfer the blueberries to the
prepared baking tray in a single layer, ensuring
they're not clumped together. Put the tray in the
freezer for at least 3-4 hours. Once frozen, divide
into 4 portions and transfer to freezer-safe
containers or bags before returning to the
freezer for up to 1 month.

Frozen chocolate & raspberry bark

serves 16   prep time 10 minutes + freezing

1 1 1   36 kcal per serving

Line a shallow 32cm x 22cm baking tray with baking paper. Put 500g **0% fat natural Greek yogurt** and 3 tablespoons **clear honey** into a bowl and stir to combine. Transfer half the mixture to a separate bowl, sift over 3 tablespoons **cocoa powder** and stir to combine. Crush 125g **raspberries** with the back of a spoon and swirl them into the yogurt without the cocoa. Pour the chocolate yogurt onto the prepared tray, followed by the raspberry yogurt, and swirl together with a knife. Dot with 125g raspberries and scatter over 5g grated **dark chocolate**, then freeze for at least 6 hours. Break into 16 shards and keep in freezer-safe containers or bags for up to 1 month.

For the weekend

BRUNCH

140 Homemade beans on toast

142 Breakfast tacos with avocado & lime sauce
Hotdog hash

143 Smoked salmon sharing rösti

144 Pumpkin pie pancakes

SUNDAY LUNCH

146 Roast pork with onion gravy

148 Roasted lamb with salsa verde beans

150 Creamed greens
Zesty asparagus, beans & peas

151 Herbed crushed new potatoes

WEEKEND DINNER

152 Cheese & onion pie with minted greens

154 Turkey meatball sliders

156 Pulled chicken bao buns

158 Chilli crab pasta

160 Soy salmon with sweet & sour aubergines

162 Crispy gnocchi with ham hock & shredded greens

164 Aubergine & lentil puttanesca with Parma-wrapped cod

166 Sriracha pork chops with celeriac & butter bean mash

WEEKEND BAKES

168 Sticky pudding with apple crisps

170 Apricot tarte tatin

172 Chocolate financiers
Coffee & walnut angel cake

MEMBERS' FAVOURITE

Homemade beans on toast

serves 4   prep time 10 minutes   cook time 35 minutes

  289 kcal
per serving

Get bags more flavour from this popular British classic by making your very own beans to pile high on hot toasted sandwich thins.

Calorie controlled cooking spray

1 small red onion, finely sliced

100g smoked bacon medallions, roughly chopped

2 garlic cloves, finely chopped

1½ teaspoons smoked paprika

1½ teaspoons mustard powder

1 teaspoon ground cumin

1 tablespoon tomato purée

400g tin chopped tomatoes

150ml vegetable stock, made with ½ stock cube

Few sprigs fresh thyme, plus extra leaves to garnish

400g tin haricot beans, drained and rinsed

400g tin cannellini beans, drained and rinsed

4 brown sandwich thins

1 Mist a nonstick pan with cooking spray and fry the onion over a medium heat for 6-8 minutes until softened. Add the bacon and garlic and fry for 3-4 minutes, then add the paprika, mustard powder and cumin and cook for 1 minute.

2 Add the tomato purée and cook, stirring, for 1 minute, then stir in the tomatoes, stock and thyme sprigs. Season and bring to a simmer. Cook for 15 minutes, then stir in the beans, season and cook for a final 5 minutes. Remove and discard the thyme.

3 Split and toast the sandwich thins and serve with the beans spooned over the top, garnished with the extra thyme leaves.

Change it up

For an extra smoky boost, use 1 tablespoon chipotle paste instead of the tomato purée. The SmartPoints will remain the same.

Breakfast tacos with avocado & lime sauce

serves 4   prep time 5 minutes   cook time 10 minutes

     325 kcal per serving

To make the sauce, blitz together 70g **avocado**, 75g **low-fat natural yogurt** and the juice of ½ **lime** in a mini food processor until smooth, then season to taste and set aside. Warm 4 **WW Protein Wraps** in a hot frying pan, then set aside and cover with a clean, dry tea towel to keep warm. Mist the same frying pan with **calorie controlled cooking spray** then fry 1 sliced **green chilli** and ½ teaspoon **ground cumin** over a medium heat for 1-3 minutes. Pour in 8 lightly beaten **eggs** and scramble for 3-5 minutes, until cooked through. Top the wraps with the scrambled eggs, 200g quartered **cherry tomatoes**, 2 tablespoons chopped **fresh coriander** and ½ finely sliced **red onion**, then drizzle with the avocado sauce and serve with lime wedges.

Hotdog hash

**serves 4   prep time 10 minutes
cook time 25 minutes**

      367 kcal per serving

Cut 500g **potatoes** into 1cm cubes and cook in a pan of boiling water for 5 minutes until just tender. Drain, and leave in the pan to steam dry. Meanwhile, mist a large nonstick lidded frying pan with **calorie controlled cooking spray** and fry 8 **chicken frankfurters** (we used Herta), cut into bite-size pieces, over a medium heat for 5-6 minutes until starting to crisp. Transfer to a plate. Add 2 finely chopped **red peppers** and 1 finely chopped **onion** to the pan, season, then cover and cook for 7-8 minutes. Mist the vegetables with more cooking spray, then stir in the potatoes and 2 chopped **garlic** cloves. Cook, stirring occasionally, for another 5-6 minutes, then return the frankfurters to the pan along with 1 chopped **spring onion**. Meanwhile, mist a large frying pan with cooking spray and fry 4 **eggs** for 3-4 minutes until the whites are crisp and the yolks soft. Serve the hash topped with the eggs and 1 shredded spring onion.

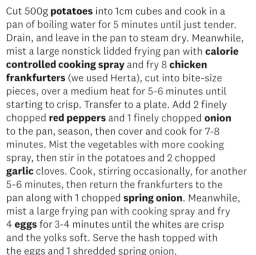

Smoked salmon sharing rösti

**serves 4   prep time 10 minutes
cook time 10 minutes**

6 **4** **2**   750 kcal per serving

Grate 350g **new potatoes** and 350g **carrots** then put into a clean tea towel and squeeze out any excess liquid. Mist a large nonstick ovenproof frying pan with **calorie controlled cooking spray** and set over a medium-high heat. Add the potato and carrots, spreading them evenly across the pan, and cook for 5 minutes. Heat the grill to high. Roughly break up the rösti with the spatula, then season. Add 1 beaten **egg** and mix it into the veg, then put the pan under the grill for 5 minutes until the top of the rösti is crisp. Meanwhile, put 220g **young leaf spinach** into a colander set over the sink, and pour over a full kettle of boiling water. Leave to wilt, then squeeze out any excess water. In a small bowl, mix together 4 tablespoons **half-fat crème fraîche** and ½ tablespoon chopped **fresh chives** and **dill** then season to taste. Serve the rösti with the spinach, 120g **smoked salmon**, crème fraîche mix, **lemon** wedges and extra herbs.

Pumpkin pie pancakes

serves 4   **prep time 10 minutes**   **cook time 15 minutes**

   278 kcal per serving

American-style pancakes are always a popular sweet brunch option – especially when they're really fluffy and full of interesting flavours.

220ml semi-skimmed milk

170g tinned pumpkin purée

1 large egg

3 tablespoons maple syrup

170g self-raising flour

½ teaspoon baking powder

2 teaspoons mixed spice, plus an extra ¼ teaspoon to serve

Calorie controlled cooking spray

140g quark

Pared zest of 1 orange, to serve

1   Preheat the oven to 160°C, fan 140°C, gas mark 3. Whisk together the milk, pumpkin purée, egg and half of the maple syrup in a small bowl. Combine the flour, baking powder and mixed spice in a separate medium mixing bowl, then whisk the wet ingredients into the dry until just combined.

2   Mist a large nonstick frying pan with cooking spray and set over a medium heat. Spoon in half the batter to make 4 pancakes. Cook for 3 minutes on each side, then transfer to a baking tray and keep warm in the oven while you repeat with the remaining batter to make 4 more pancakes.

3   Mix the quark with the remaining maple syrup. Serve the pancakes topped with the quark, extra mixed spice and orange zest.

MEMBERS' FAVOURITE

Roast pork with onion gravy

serves 6   prep time 20 minutes   cook time 1 hour 5 minutes

    379 kcal
per serving

Who doesn't love a Sunday roast? This all-in-one traybake roast is the one members call on when they want a recipe that's big on classic flavours and light on washing up.

6 carrots, cut into 1cm chunks

3 red onions, cut into wedges

900g new potatoes, halved or quartered if large

3 apples, cored and cut into wedges

3 garlic cloves, unpeeled

2 tablespoons wholegrain mustard

3 teaspoons clear honey

500ml chicken stock, made with 1 stock cube

Calorie controlled cooking spray

1 tablespoon dried mixed herbs

Grated zest of 1½ lemons

600g pork tenderloin fillet

100g onion chutney

1 tablespoon cornflour

1 Preheat the oven to 190°C, fan 170°C, gas mark 5. Put the vegetables, apples and garlic into a roasting tin. In a small jug, combine the mustard with the honey and 150ml of the chicken stock, then pour the mixture over the veg. Season well, cover with kitchen foil and roast for 25 minutes.

2 Meanwhile, mist a nonstick frying pan with cooking spray and set over a medium heat. Mix the dried herbs with the lemon zest on a dinner plate. Mist the pork all over with cooking spray, season well, then roll it in the herb mixture. Sear the pork in the pan, turning regularly, for 3-4 minutes until browned all over then remove from the heat.

3 Take the roasting tin out of the oven and remove the foil. Put the pork on top of the vegetables and return the tin, uncovered, to the oven. Increase the temperature to 200°C, fan 180°C, gas mark 6 and roast for 30-40 minutes, or until the pork is cooked through.

4 Meanwhile, make the onion gravy. Put the onion chutney and remaining stock in a small pan and put over a medium-low heat. In a small jug, combine the cornflour with 2 tablespoons water and add to the pan. Simmer, whisking constantly, for 2-3 minutes, or until thickened.

5 Slice the pork and serve with the vegetables and onion gravy.

Roasted lamb with salsa verde beans

serves 6   prep time 15 minutes + resting   cook time 35 minutes

   287 kcal
per serving

A proper Sunday roast deserves a proper joint of meat and this melt-in-the-mouth butterflied and rolled lamb leg is a real showstopper.

600g butterflied leg of lamb, visible fat removed

1 teaspoon olive oil

1 teaspoon fresh thyme leaves

2 teaspoons finely chopped fresh rosemary

2 x 400g tins cannellini beans, drained and rinsed

FOR THE SALSA VERDE

1 teaspoon olive oil

½ tablespoon red wine vinegar

2 tablespoons chopped fresh basil

2 tablespoons chopped fresh flat-leaf parsley

1 tablespoon chopped fresh mint, plus extra to serve

½ small garlic clove, crushed

1 tablespoon capers, drained, rinsed and finely chopped

2 anchovies in oil, drained and finely chopped

Grated zest of ½ lemon

1   Preheat the oven to 200°C, fan 180°C, gas mark 6. Rub the lamb all over with the oil, thyme and rosemary, then season well. Roll the lamb and secure with kitchen string.

2   Heat a large nonstick frying pan over a high heat, add the lamb and sear for 2-3 minutes on each side to seal and brown the meat. Transfer the lamb to a roasting tin and roast for 25-30 minutes. Remove from the oven, loosely cover with foil and set aside to rest for 10 minutes before carving.

3   While the lamb is resting, make the salsa verde. Mix all the salsa verde ingredients in a small bowl with 1 tablespoon water. Season to taste. Put the beans into a frying pan with 1 tablespoon water and gently heat until just warm, then stir in most of the salsa verde.

4   Serve the salsa verde beans with the sliced lamb, the remaining salsa verde and a few extra mint leaves.

Cook's tip

Rolling and securing the lamb looks neater and allows for easy carving and portioning. But if you don't feel confident rolling it, just cook the butterflied joint as it is. It will only need 20 minutes in the oven.

Creamed greens

serves 6 **prep time 10 minutes**
cook time 5 minutes

   56 kcal per serving

Remove and discard the stalks from 100g **kale** and the tough veins from 100g **Savoy cabbage**, then finely shred and set aside. Trim and slice 150g **Brussels sprouts** and set aside. Mist a large nonstick frying pan with **calorie controlled cooking spray** and cook the veg over a medium heat for 3-4 minutes, stirring regularly, until wilted and tender – add a splash of water to help the vegetables wilt if they seem too dry. Mix 120g **half-fat crème fraîche**, 1 teaspoon **Dijon mustard** and a pinch of **ground nutmeg** together in a jug with a splash of water. Season then stir through the veg until warmed through.

Zesty asparagus, beans & peas

serves 6 **prep time 5 minutes**
cook time 5 minutes

   61 kcal per serving

Bring a pan of water to the boil. Add 200g **fine green beans** and cook for 3 minutes, then add 250g **asparagus tips**, halved lengthways, and 200g **frozen garden peas** and cook for a final 2 minutes. Drain and refresh under cold running water then transfer the veg to a serving dish. In a small bowl, combine 1 tablespoon finely chopped **fresh mint**, the pared zest of ½ **lemon**, ¼ finely chopped **red onion** and 2 teaspoons **extra-virgin olive oil**. Season then toss through the hot vegetables.

Herbed crushed new potatoes

serves 6　　**prep time 5 minutes**　　**cook time 40 minutes**

3　**3**　**0**　　106 kcal per serving

Preheat the oven to 200°C, fan 180°C, gas mark 6.
Cook 750g **new potatoes** in a pan of boiling water
for 15 minutes until just tender, then drain and lightly
crush with the back of a spoon – you don't want
them to fall apart completely. Put the potatoes
onto a baking tray and mist with **calorie controlled
cooking spray**. Season and bake for 20 minutes. Mist
a small nonstick frying pan with cooking spray and
fry 4 chopped **smoked bacon medallions** over a
medium heat for 3-4 minutes. Add 2 thickly sliced
garlic cloves and cook for another 2 minutes then
remove from the heat. Add the bacon and garlic to
the baking tray, along with the stripped leaves of
2 **fresh rosemary** sprigs and toss to combine.
Bake for a final 5 minutes until crisp and golden.

MEMBERS' FAVOURITE

Cheese & onion pie with minted greens

serves 6   prep time 10 minutes   cook time 50 minutes

    361 kcal per serving

A flaky pastry-topped pie is perennially popular and this easy-to-make version makes an impressive centrepiece for a meat-free weekend dinner.

400g potatoes, cut into 3cm pieces

Calorie controlled cooking spray

2 large onions, finely chopped

2 garlic cloves, finely chopped

200g half-fat Cheddar, grated

2 tablespoons chopped fresh flat-leaf parsley

3 eggs, lightly beaten

320g sheet ready rolled light puff pastry (you'll use 160g)

FOR THE MINTED GREENS

240g Tenderstem broccoli

240g frozen peas

1½ tablespoons low-fat spread

2 tablespoons chopped fresh mint

Change it up
Add some heat to the filling by stirring ½-1 teaspoon English mustard through the filling at the end of Step 2. The SmartPoints will stay the same.

---

1 Cook the potatoes in a large pan of boiling water for 10-15 minutes until tender, then drain and allow to steam dry in the sieve or colander used for draining.

2 Meanwhile, mist a large nonstick frying pan with cooking spray and set over a medium heat. Add the onions and cook for 15 minutes until soft and starting to caramelise. Add the garlic and cook for another 1 minute, then transfer to a large bowl along with the cooked potatoes, cheese and parsley. Reserve 1 tablespoon of the beaten eggs, then add the rest to the bowl. Season well and gently stir to combine.

3 Preheat the oven to 200°C, fan 180°C, gas mark 6. Put the cheese and onion mixture into a 24cm shallow pie dish. Unroll the pastry and lay it over the top of the filling. Trim off the excess pastry and crimp the edges of the pie. Brush all over with the reserved beaten egg and cut a slit in the centre of the pastry to allow steam to escape while it's cooking. Bake for 30-35 minutes, until the pastry is puffed and golden.

4 While the pie is baking, make the minted greens. Cook the broccoli in a pan of boiling water for 3 minutes, then add the peas and cook for another 1 minute or until both are tender. Drain, return to the pan and add the spread and mint. Stir until the spread has melted then season to taste.

5 Serve the pie with the veg on the side.

Turkey meatball sliders

serves 4   prep time 10 minutes   cook time 35 minutes

   365 kcal per serving

If you love tucking into a burger at the end of the working week and want new inspiration, these meltingly good oven-baked sliders could be just what you're looking for.

1 red onion, coarsely grated

2 garlic cloves, crushed

1 teaspoon dried oregano

1 tablespoon finely chopped fresh basil leaves, plus extra to serve

400g turkey breast mince

400g passata

1 teaspoon dried mixed herbs

8 x 35g mini white slider rolls (we used Asda)

80g grated light mozzarella

Mixed salad leaves, to serve

1 Preheat the oven to 200°C, fan 180°C, gas mark 6. Mix the onion, garlic, oregano, basil and turkey mince together in a mixing bowl and season well. Shape the mixture into 8 small meatballs. Pour the passata into a pan, stir in the dried mixed herbs and bring to a gentle simmer. Poach the meatballs in the sauce for 10-12 minutes.

2 Cut each bread roll in half, then put the bottoms of the rolls into a small baking dish – they need to be tightly packed together. Spoon over the meatballs and sauce, then scatter over the mozzarella. Cover with kitchen foil and bake for 10 minutes.

3 Remove the foil, put the bread roll tops over the meatballs then bake, uncovered, for 10 minutes.

4 Serve 2 sliders per person, with the salad and extra basil leaves.

Pulled chicken bao buns

serves 4   prep time 10 minutes   cook time 3 hours

   312 kcal per serving

Planning a night in front of the telly? Bao buns are perfect for chilling out. Toss everything into the slow cooker and it'll be ready by episode three of your box-set marathon.

4 x 165g skinless chicken breast fillets

2 tablespoons dark soy sauce

1 tablespoon clear honey

2 tablespoons oyster sauce

½ tablespoon rice wine vinegar

1 tablespoon finely grated ginger

3 garlic cloves, finely sliced

1 red chilli, sliced

2 teaspoons cornflour

4 x 30g bao buns

1 large carrot, cut into matchsticks

4 spring onions, trimmed and shredded

Coriander leaves, to serve

1. Put the chicken into a slow cooker. Mix the soy sauce, honey, oyster sauce, vinegar, ginger, garlic and chilli together in a small bowl, then pour over the chicken. Cover and cook on low for 3 hours, then transfer the chicken to a plate, shred with forks and keep warm.

2. Pour the liquid from the slow cooker into a small pan and whisk in the cornflour. Gently simmer over a medium-low heat until the sauce is thick enough to coat the back of a spoon, then stir in the shredded chicken and heat through.

3. Heat the bao buns to pack instructions, then stuff with the chicken, carrot and spring onions. Scatter over the coriander leaves and serve.

- The pulled chicken can be frozen in an airtight container for up to 1 month.

Cook's tip

Scatter 5g chopped roasted peanuts over each of the bao buns just before serving. The recipe will no longer be nut free.

Chilli crab pasta

serves 4   prep time 10 minutes   cook time 10 minutes

   265 kcal per serving

All you need for a restaurant-worthy pasta dish that's ready in 20 minutes is a handful of good-quality ingredients and a clever hack using fresh lasagne sheets.

Calorie controlled spray

1 garlic clove, finely sliced

250g cherry tomatoes, halved

150ml chicken stock made with ½ stock cube

100g medium-fat soft cheese

100g young leaf spinach

4 x 60g sheets fresh lasagne

300g white crab meat

1 red chilli, deseeded and finely chopped, plus extra to serve

Finely grated zest of ½ lemon

100g ricotta

½ tablespoon chopped fresh chives

1 Mist a large nonstick frying pan with cooking spray and fry the garlic over a medium heat for 1 minute. Add the tomatoes and cook for a further 3-4 minutes, adding a little of the stock every minute or so. Once the tomatoes have started to break down slightly, add the soft cheese and any remaining stock. Stir to melt the cheese and create a smooth sauce. Add the spinach, cover the pan and leave to wilt. Once wilted, season to taste and keep warm.

2 Put the lasagne sheets in a large baking dish and then cover with boiling water from the kettle and leave for 2 minutes. Meanwhile, combine the crab, chilli, lemon zest and ricotta in a bowl.

3 When you're ready to serve, remove a sheet of lasagne from the water to a chopping board, and cut it into three strips. Place one strip in a warmed pasta bowl and add a large tablespoonful of the crab mixture at one end, folding the pasta in a ribbon around it. Repeat with the other two pieces of pasta and another 2 tablespoons of crab. Spoon over a quarter of the tomato spinach sauce and scatter with chives and the extra chilli. Repeat with the remaining ingredients then serve.

Soy salmon with sweet & sour aubergines

serves 4   prep time 10 minutes   cook time 20 minutes

   426 kcal per serving

The richness of salmon paired with the sharp tang of these tender braised aubergines makes for a mouthwatering main that's special enough to serve to guests.

4 x 130g skinless salmon fillets

4 tablespoons dark soy sauce

2 teaspoons grated ginger

1 tablespoon tomato purée

1 tablespoon cider vinegar

1 tablespoon agave syrup

1 red chilli, deseeded and finely sliced

Calorie controlled cooking spray

2 aubergines, cut into 2cm cubes

160g basmati rice

Handful fresh coriander, chopped, plus extra leaves to serve

3 spring onions, trimmed and shredded, plus extra to serve

Lime wedges, to serve

1   Preheat the oven to 200°C, fan 180°C, gas mark 6. Put the salmon in a baking dish and pour over the soy sauce. Set aside to marinate for 5 minutes, then roast for 12-15 minutes until the salmon is cooked through.

2   Meanwhile, in a small jug, combine the ginger, tomato purée, vinegar, agave syrup, chilli and 2 tablespoons cold water, then set aside.

3   Mist a large nonstick lidded frying pan with cooking spray and set over a medium heat. Add the aubergines and cook for 15 minutes until browned (add a splash of water if they start to stick), then add the sweet and sour sauce mixture. Cook, covered, for 3 minutes.

4   While the salmon is roasting and the aubergines are braising, cook the rice in a pan of boiling water to pack instructions. Drain then stir through the coriander and spring onions.

5   Serve the rice with the salmon, aubergines and lime wedges, garnished with the extra coriander and spring onions.

Crispy gnocchi with ham hock & shredded greens

serves 4   prep time 5 minutes   cook time 15 minutes

   320 kcal per serving

A plate of potato gnocchi is the kind of dish that's perfect for lazy weekends. We've pan-fried them for extra crunch then tossed them with ham and a trio of crunchy veg.

Calorie controlled cooking spray

600g fresh gnocchi

80g Savoy cabbage, shredded

1 leek, trimmed and finely sliced

100g Brussels sprouts, trimmed and shredded

3 garlic cloves, thinly sliced

200ml hot chicken stock, made with ½ stock cube

2 teaspoons wholegrain mustard

90g shredded cooked ham hock

20g Parmesan, finely grated

1   Mist a large nonstick frying pan with cooking spray and set over a medium heat. Add the gnocchi and cook, turning occasionally, for 5-6 minutes until lightly golden, then transfer to a plate.

2   Mist the pan with more cooking spray, then stir-fry the cabbage, leek, sprouts and garlic for 5 minutes until tender and lightly golden.

3   Stir in the stock, mustard and ham hock, and simmer for 2 minutes, then return the gnocchi to the pan and stir until combined and heated through.

4   Serve garnished with the Parmesan.

Cook's tip
If you're not a fan of Brussels sprouts, you can simply leave them out and bump up the quantities of cabbage and leek.

Aubergine & lentil puttanesca with Parma-wrapped cod

serves 4   prep time 10 minutes   cook time 25 minutes

   356 kcal per serving

For impressive results with minimal effort, wrap thick cod fillets in Parma ham and serve with a tasty one-pot aubergine and lentil stew.

Calorie controlled cooking spray

1 aubergine, cut into 1cm cubes

1 red onion, finely chopped

2 garlic cloves, finely chopped

2 teaspoons chilli flakes

500ml passata

250ml chicken stock, made with 1 stock cube

80g sundried tomatoes in oil, drained and patted dry

80g pitted black olives in brine, drained

2 tablespoons small capers in brine, drained

250g pouch ready-cooked Puy lentils

4 x 120g skinless cod fillets

4 slices Parma ham

2 tablespoons roughly chopped fresh flat-leaf parsley, to serve

1 Mist a nonstick pan with cooking spray and set over a medium heat. Add the aubergine and onion, and cook for 10 minutes, stirring occasionally, until tender, then add the garlic and chilli flakes, and cook for another minute. Pour in the passata and stock, and gently simmer for 15 minutes, then stir in the sundried tomatoes, olives, capers and lentils.

2 Meanwhile, preheat the oven to 200°C, fan 180°C, gas mark 6, and line a baking tray with baking paper. Season the cod with freshly ground black pepper and wrap each fillet in a slice of Parma ham. Put on the prepared tray and bake for 12-15 minutes, until the cod is cooked through and the ham is crisp.

3 Divide the lentil puttanesca between plates, top with the Parma-wrapped cod and serve with the parsley scattered over the top.

Sriracha pork chops with celeriac & butter bean mash

serves 4   prep time 5 minutes   cook time 20 minutes

 502 kcal per serving

We've bought meat and three veg bang up to date by brushing a sticky Korean-style glaze over thick-cut pork chops and serving them with pan-fried greens and a no-potato mash.

4 x 200g pork chops on the bone, trimmed of excess fat

600g celeriac, peeled and cut into small chunks

400g tin butter beans, drained and rinsed

100ml semi-skimmed milk

Calorie controlled cooking spray

200g spinach

4 baby pak choi, roughly chopped

FOR THE SRIRACHA GLAZE

1 tablespoon sriracha

2 tablespoons soy sauce

½ tablespoon clear honey

1 To make the sriracha glaze, mix the sriracha, soy sauce and honey together in a mixing bowl. Add the pork chops, turn to coat then set aside.

2 Bring a pan of water to the boil and cook the celeriac for 15-20 minutes until tender, then drain and mash with the butter beans and milk. Season to taste, then set aside to keep warm.

3 Meanwhile, preheat the oven to 200°C, fan 180°C, gas mark 6 and line a baking tray with kitchen foil. Mist a large nonstick frying pan with cooking spray and set over a medium-low heat. Lift the pork from the glaze (reserving any of the liquid), and sear for 2-3 minutes on each side. Pour in the reserved marinade and simmer for 1 minute, then transfer the pork to the prepared baking tray, cover with foil and bake for 8 minutes.

4 Add the spinach and pak choi to the frying pan you used to sear the pork chops and cook, stirring, for 1-2 minutes until wilted.

5 Serve the mash topped with the vegetables and pork chops, with any pan juices drizzled over.

MEMBERS' FAVOURITE

Sticky pudding with apple crisps

serves 12   **prep time 15 minutes**   **cook time 1 hour 15 minutes**

   225 kcal per serving

This super moist and sticky traybake-style dessert is one of our most popular puds. It serves 12 so is great for large family gatherings, but will also keep in the fridge for a couple of days.

Calorie controlled cooking spray

180g pitted soft prunes, roughly chopped

2 apples, peeled, cored and grated (you'll need about 170g)

2 teaspoons vanilla extract

3 teaspoons grated ginger

6 large eggs, separated

250g self-raising flour

2 teaspoons bicarbonate of soda

Pinch of salt

280g date syrup

FOR THE APPLE CRISPS

1 apple, cored and thinly sliced

Change it up

You can use pears instead of apples in this recipe – look for firm, ripe pears, such as Conference. The SmartPoints will remain the same.

1   To make the apple crisps, preheat the oven to 140°C, fan 120°C, gas mark 1, and line a baking sheet with baking paper. Spread the slices out onto the baking sheet. Bake for 40 minutes or until crisp.

2   For the pudding, increase the oven temperature to 180°C, fan 160°C, gas mark 4. Mist a 30cm x 20cm cake tin with cooking spray and line the base and sides with baking paper.

3   Put the prunes and grated apples into a pan with 450ml water and bring to a simmer over a medium heat. Cover and cook for 5-6 minutes until softened. Set aside to cool, then transfer to a blender, add the vanilla and ginger and blitz to a purée. Scrape into to a mixing bowl and stir in the egg yolks. Sift in the flour, add the bicarbonate of soda and salt, then stir well.

4   In a separate bowl, whisk the egg whites until stiff peaks form, then fold into the prune mixture, ensuring they are fully incorporated. Pour the mixture into the prepared tin and bake for 25-30 minutes, or until a skewer inserted into the centre comes out clean.

5   Reserve 2 tablespoons of the date syrup then put the rest into a small pan and warm over a low heat until runny. Poke holes all over the pudding with a skewer, the drizzle the warm syrup all over the top while still warm. Remove from the tin and cut into 12 squares. Serve the pudding topped with the apple crisps and drizzled with the reserved date syrup.

Apricot tarte tatin

serves 8   prep time 10 minutes + cooling and standing   cook time 45 minutes

   180 kcal per serving

Sticky, buttery caramel, sweet apricots and golden flaky pastry is a classic dessert combination that everyone finds irresistible.

55g caster sugar

30g butter, chilled and diced

10 apricots, halved and stones removed

375g sheet ready rolled light puff pastry (you'll use 180g)

160g half-fat crème fraîche

1 Put the sugar in a 25cm heavy-based ovenproof frying pan and set over a medium heat. Cook until the sugar melts and then caramelises and turns amber – don't stir the sugar, but do give the pan a swirl occasionally. Add the butter and stir until melted. Continue to cook, stirring, over a medium heat for 2-3 minutes, until the caramel mixture is thick and syrupy.

2 Reduce the heat to low, add the apricots and turn to coat. Cook for 1-2 minutes, turning the apricots regularly, until they are fully coated in the syrup. Flip the apricots so they're cut-side up, then remove the pan from the heat and let cool for 20 minutes.

3 Preheat the oven to 200°C, fan 180°C, gas mark 6. Unroll the pastry then use a rolling pin to roll it out further so that it's 3cm wider than it was originally. Use a 26cm plate as a template to cut out a circle, discarding the trimmings. Drape the pastry over the apricots and push down the sides. Cut 3 slits in the centre to allow steam to escape, then bake for 25-30 minutes, until the pastry is puffed and golden. Let stand for 20 minutes.

4 Put a large serving plate on top of the frying pan, then carefully but quickly invert the pan so that the tarte tatin drops onto the plate. Slice and serve warm with the crème fraîche spooned over.

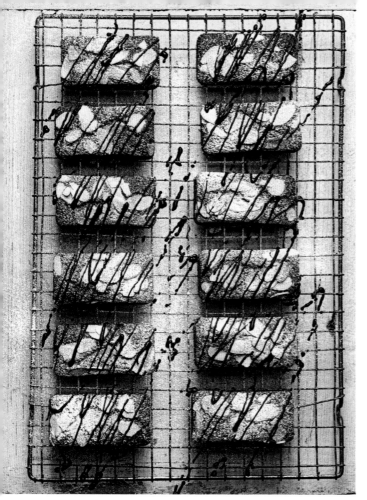

Chocolate financiers

makes 12   prep time 15 minutes   cook time 25 minutes

     153 kcal per financier

Preheat the oven to 180°C, fan 160°C, gas mark 4. Mist a 12-hole nonstick shallow mini loaf tin with **calorie controlled cooking spray**. Melt 90g **low-fat spread** in the microwave and leave it to cool while you prep the other ingredients. Put 75g **ground almonds** in a large bowl. Sift over 155g **icing sugar**, 55g **plain flour**, 20g **cocoa powder** and ½ teaspoon **baking powder**. Lightly whisk 4 **egg whites**, until just starting to foam, then add them to the bowl of dry ingredients along with the cooled melted spread and whisk to combine. Spoon the mixture into the prepared tin, scatter over 10g **flaked almonds** and bake for 20 minutes. Remove from the tin and let cool on a wire rack. Dust with 5g icing sugar, then melt 10g **dark chocolate** in the microwave to drizzle over. The financiers will keep in an airtight container for up to 3 days.

Coffee & walnut angel cake

serves 12   prep time 25 minutes cook time 35 minutes

     165 kcal per serving

Preheat the oven to 190°C, fan 170°C, gas mark 5. Sift 140g **plain flour** and 50g **icing sugar** into a bowl and set aside. In a large bowl, whisk 12 **egg whites** with an electric whisk until foamy. Whisk in 1½ teaspoons **cream of tartar** and ¼ teaspoon **salt**, then gradually whisk in 150g icing sugar, one spoonful at a time, until stiff peaks form. Make 60ml **coffee** with 1 teaspoon instant coffee granules, then whisk this into the egg white mixture along with 1 teaspoon **vanilla extract**. In 3 batches, fold the flour mixture into the meringue mixture, using a metal spoon, until there are no lumps – be careful not to overmix. Scrape into an ungreased 24cm ring tin and bake for 30-35 minutes, or until puffed and golden. Turn the tin upside down on a wire rack and leave to cool completely. Run a palette knife around the tin to loosen the cake and gently let it drop out. Set aside, base-side up, on a cake stand. To make the glaze, make 1½ tablespoons coffee with ¼ teaspoon instant coffee granules, then stir into 90g icing sugar until smooth and combined. Pour over the surface of the cake, allowing it to drip down over the sides, then scatter over 20g shaved **toasted walnuts**.

Entertaining

COCKTAILS & CANAPÉS

176 Cranberry & thyme gin cocktail
    Sesame prawns with sriracha
178 Sweet potato & chickpea rolls
    Courgette bites with feta dip
179 Balsamic beetroot
    & ricotta toasts
180 Cauliflower 'wings' with
    chickpea dip

CELEBRATION MAINS

182 Griddled rump steak with
    chips & mustard 'mayo'
184 Barbecued miso aubergines
    Smoky salmon & chorizo skewers
186 Turkish steak pittas
188 Beer-glazed chicken
    skewers with succotash

190 Scallop & leek risotto
192 Herb-crusted side of salmon
194 Cauliflower wellington
196 Honey & soy-glazed ham

CELEBRATION DESSERTS

198 Chocolate celebration cake
200 Raspberry & coconut
    soufflés
202 Fig & mascarpone
    roulade
204 Peanut butter
    & banana ice-cream
    sandwiches
    Lemon mousse with
    ginger crumb
205 Tropical fruit Charlotte

MEMBERS' FAVOURITE

Cranberry & thyme gin cocktail

makes 6   prep time 5 minutes + infusing   cook time 10 minutes

   102 kcal per cocktail

Take a tip from fellow members and serve this next-level G&T at your next gathering.

100g fresh or frozen cranberries, plus extra to garnish

50g granulated sugar

A few large twists of orange peel, plus extra to garnish

3 sprigs thyme, plus extra to garnish

150ml gin

300ml low-calorie tonic water

1   Put the cranberries, sugar and orange peel in a small pan set over a low heat. Pour over 175ml water and bring to a simmer. Cook for 5 minutes, then add the thyme sprigs and bring to the boil. Remove from the heat, cover and set aside for 20 minutes to infuse. Strain through a fine mesh sieve and then set the cranberry and thyme syrup aside to cool completely.

2   To serve, fill 6 chilled short tumblers with ice, pour over the syrup and gin then top up with the tonic water. Stir and serve garnished with the extra cranberries, orange peel and thyme sprigs.

Sesame prawns with sriracha

serves 6   prep time 5 minutes

   132 kcal per serving

These no-cook posh nibbles look impressive but couldn't be easier to make.

4 tablespoons sesame seeds

2 x 180g packs cooked king prawns

2 tablespoons sweet chilli sauce

2 spring onions, shredded

¼ cucumber, cut into matchsticks

4 tablespoons reduced-fat mayonnaise

1 tablespoon lime juice

½ tablespoon sriracha

1   Toast the sesame seeds in a dry frying pan set over a medium-low heat for 1-2 minutes until golden. Remove from the pan and spread out on a large plate.

2   In a small bowl, toss the cooked prawns with the sweet chilli sauce, then press into the sesame seeds and transfer to a serving plate along with the shredded spring onions and cucumber.

3   Mix the mayonnaise with the lime juice and sriracha and transfer to a small bowl. Put on the plate with the prawns and serve with cocktail sticks.

Change it up

For a citrus twist on the gin cocktail, make a grapefruit and tarragon syrup. Simmer the peel and juice of ½ pink grapefruit (175ml juice), 1½ tablespoons lemon juice and 50g sugar in a pan for 5 minutes. Add 4 sprigs tarragon, bring to the boil then remove from the heat and infuse for 20 minutes. Strain and serve as in Step 2, left, garnished with extra tarragon. The SmartPoints will remain the same.

Sweet potato & chickpea rolls

makes 18   prep time 20 minutes   cook time 50 minutes

     106 kcal per roll

Preheat the oven to 200°C, fan 180°C, gas mark 6 and line a baking tray with baking paper. Peel and cut 500g **sweet potatoes** into 1cm pieces, then put into a roasting tin and mist with **calorie controlled cooking spray**. Add 1 teaspoon **smoked paprika**, ½ teaspoon **chilli powder**, 1 teaspoon **ground cumin** and ¼ teaspoon **ground cinnamon**. Cut 2 **onions** into thin wedges and add these to the pan with 2 crushed **garlic** cloves. Season, toss together and roast for 30 minutes. Drain and rinse a 400g tin **chickpeas**, then add these to the tin and roast for 5 minutes. Tip into a bowl then lightly mash so the mixture holds together, but is chunky. Lay 2 sheets of **filo pastry** alongside each other, overlapping by 10cm. Brush with ½ tablespoon **vegetable oil**, top with another 2 sheets of filo, brush again with ½ tablespoon vegetable oil, then lay a final 2 sheets of filo on top. Spoon the filling along one of the long edges of filo and brush the rest of the pastry with ¼ tablespoon vegetable oil. Roll into a sausage shape, then brush the top with ¼ tablespoon vegetable oil and scatter over 2 teaspoons **poppy seeds**. Cut into 18 rolls and put on the tray. Bake for 15 minutes then serve.

Courgette bites with feta dip

serves 6   prep time 15 minutes   cook time 30 minutes

     82 kcal per serving

Grate 2 **courgettes** (around 600g), put into a colander set over the sink and sprinkle with a little **salt**. Leave for 30 minutes then squeeze out any excess water and put the courgette into a bowl. Preheat the oven to 200°C, fan 180°C, gas mark 6 and line a baking tray with baking paper. Chop the leaves of 4 **fresh mint** sprigs and add to the courgette with 2 chopped **spring onions**, a pinch of **ground nutmeg** and 1 tablespoon **self-raising flour**. Mix to combine, then season and stir in 1 large beaten **egg**. Put 40g **panko breadcrumbs** in a bowl. Roll spoonfuls of the courgette mixture in the crumbs, then put them on the prepared baking tray – you'll have enough for 24 bites. Mist with **calorie controlled cooking spray** and bake for 25-30 minutes. To make the dip, blitz **100g fat-free natural yogurt** and 50g **light feta** in a mini food processor then put in a bowl. Arrange on a platter and serve 4 bites per person.

Balsamic beetroot & ricotta toasts

serves 6   prep time 10 minutes   cook time 10 minutes

3 **3** **3**   119 kcal per serving

Drain 300g **cooked beetroot** (not in vinegar) and cut into thin wedges. Mist a nonstick frying pan with **calorie controlled cooking spray** and cook the beetroot over a medium heat for 2-3 minutes. Add 4 tablespoons **balsamic vinegar** and 1 teaspoon **cumin seeds**, then increase the heat to medium-high and cook for 2-3 minutes, stirring, until the beetroot is sticky. Preheat the grill to high. Cut ½ **baguette** (125g) into 18 x 5mm rounds, then mist with cooking spray and rub with the cut sides of 1 halved **garlic** clove. Grill for 1-2 minutes, turning once, until just golden then arrange on a serving platter. Combine 125g **ricotta** with the grated zest of ½ **lemon**, then season and spoon onto the toasts. Top with 40g **watercress** leaves and the balsamic beetroot. Serve 3 toasts per person.

Cauliflower 'wings' with chickpea dip

serves 6   prep time 20 minutes   cook time 30 minutes

   164 kcal per serving

These brilliant vegan bites, with a sriracha drizzle and accompanying creamy dip, make clever use of a tin of chickpeas.

400g tin chickpeas, water drained and reserved

1 tablespoon plain flour

40g panko breadcrumbs, lightly crushed

1 teaspoon paprika

½ teaspoon ground cumin

¼ teaspoon garlic powder

400g small cauliflower florets

80ml sriracha

1 teaspoon agave syrup

2 garlic cloves, roughly chopped

2 tablespoons plain soya yogurt

Grated zest and juice of ½ lemon, plus lemon wedges to serve

1   Preheat the oven to 200°C, fan 180°C, gas mark 6. Line a large baking sheet with baking paper.

2   To make a batter, put half of the reserved chickpea water into a bowl and whisk with a hand-held electric whisk until light and foamy. Add the flour and beat again until combined.

3   In a shallow bowl, combine the panko breadcrumbs with the paprika, cumin and garlic powder, then season well.

4   In batches, toss the cauliflower in the batter, then roll it in the panko breadcrumb mixture to coat. Transfer to the prepared baking sheet and bake for 20 minute. Combine the sriracha and agave syrup, then drizzle over the cauliflower and bake for a further 10 minutes, until golden.

5   Meanwhile, put the chickpeas into a food processor with the garlic and blitz to a chunky purée. Add the soya yogurt, lemon juice and remaining chickpea water and blitz until smooth and combined. Season to taste, then scrape into a small bowl and garnish with the lemon zest. Arrange the cauliflower 'wings' on a platter and serve the dip and lemon wedges on the side.

MEMBERS' FAVOURITE

Griddled rump steak with chips & mustard 'mayo'

serves 6   prep time 15 minutes   cook time 35 minutes

   494 kcal per serving

Bring a gastro-pub vibe to your next dinner party by serving a dish that has the member stamp of approval – juicy steaks with a trio of good-for-you veggie chips.

450g butternut squash (skin-on), cut into chips

450g sweet potato, scrubbed and cut into chips

450g potatoes, scrubbed and cut into chips

Calorie controlled cooking spray

1½ teaspoons dried oregano

6 x 225g rump steaks, trimmed of visible fat

6 small garlic cloves, very thinly sliced

480g green beans

FOR THE MUSTARD 'MAYO'

300g 0% fat natural Greek yogurt

1½ teaspoons Dijon mustard

1½ tablespoons lemon juice

1   Preheat the oven to 200°C, fan 180°C, gas mark 6. Arrange the chips on a very large baking tray in a single layer, mist all over with cooking spray and scatter over the oregano. Season well and bake for 35 minutes, shaking the tray occasionally, until crisp and golden.

2   Meanwhile, to make the 'mayo', combine the yogurt, mustard and lemon juice in a small bowl, then season to taste and set aside.

3   Mist the steaks with cooking spray, season well and scatter over the garlic slices. Mist a large nonstick griddle pan with cooking spray, set over a high heat and sear the steaks for 2 minutes on each side for rare, 3 minutes each side for medium and 4 minutes for well done. Remove to a plate, cover with foil and let rest for 5 minutes. You'll need to do this in batches.

4   While the steaks are resting, cook the beans in a pan of boiling water for 4-5 minutes until tender. Drain.

5   Serve the garlic steaks with the chips, green beans and mustard 'mayo'.

Change it up
Omit the garlic and swap the rump steaks for 6 x 140g tuna steaks – you'll only need to griddle them for 1-2 minutes on each side.

Smoky salmon & chorizo skewers

serves 6   prep time 20 minutes + marinating   cook time 15 minutes

   257 kcal per serving

Preheat the barbecue. Cut 600g **skinless salmon fillets** into 3-4cm pieces, then put in a large dish. In a jug, mix together 2 teaspoons **sweet smoked paprika**, 1 teaspoon **dried oregano**, the juice of 1 **orange**, 1 tablespoon **olive oil** and 1 teaspoon **sherry vinegar**, then season. Pour over the salmon, then cover and marinate for 30 minutes. Meanwhile, make a gremolata: finely chop a handful of **fresh flat-leaf parsley** and 2 small **garlic** cloves, then add these to a small bowl with the pared zests of ½ **orange** and 1 **lemon**. Season and set aside. Chop 1 red and 1 yellow **pepper** into 3-4cm pieces and thinly slice 60g **chorizo**. Thread the salmon onto 6 large skewers, alternating with the peppers and chorizo. Barbecue for 10-12 minutes, turning every now and then, until the salmon is cooked through. Serve the skewers with the gremolata and lemon wedges.

Barbecued miso aubergines

serves 6   prep time 15 minutes + marinating   cook time 20 minutes

    124 kcal per serving

Preheat the barbecue, then make a marinade by whisking together 100ml **mirin**, 3 tablespoons **white miso paste**, 1 teaspoon **maple syrup**, 1 tablespoon **sesame oil**, 1 teaspoon **chilli flakes** and some **freshly ground black pepper**. Halve 6 small **aubergines** lengthways then score the flesh and brush with three-quarters of the marinade. Set aside to marinate for 30 minutes. Barbecue the aubergines, flesh-side down, for 10-15 minutes until soft and charred – keep them moving while they're cooking to prevent the flesh sticking to the grill. Mist the skin of the aubergines with **calorie controlled cooking spray** then carefully turn and barbecue on the other side for 5-8 minutes. Remove from the barbecue and brush the charred tops with a little of the remaining marinade. Arrange on a platter, drizzle with the last of the marinade, then serve garnished with 2 sliced **spring onions**, a handful of **fresh coriander** leaves and 20g **crispy fried onions**.

Turkish steak pittas

serves 6   prep time 5 minutes + marinating   cook time 10 minutes

   411 kcal
per serving

Tender marinated steak is stuffed into griddled pitta bread pockets with a pomegranate and mint salad, then served with a garlicky yogurt sauce.

3 x 225g rump steaks

6 x 60g pitta breads

70g rocket

FOR THE MARINADE

2 teaspoons cumin seeds

1 teaspoon ground coriander

1½ tablespoons pomegranate molasses

2 teaspoons agave syrup

2 teaspoons olive oil

FOR THE SAUCE

250g strained 0% fat natural Greek yogurt

2 tablespoons tahini

2 garlic cloves, chopped

30g rocket

FOR THE SALAD

½ red onion, thinly sliced

200g pomegranate seeds

½ tablespoon pomegranate molasses

Large handful fresh mint, leaves picked and torn

1   To make the marinade, combine all the marinade ingredients in a dish, then season well. Add the steaks and turn to coat, then cover and marinate for 1 hour at room temperature.

2   Preheat the barbecue. To make the sauce, put the yogurt, tahini and garlic into a food processor with some salt. Blitz until combined, then add the 30g of the rocket. Pulse until combined, then scrape into a bowl and set aside.

3   To make the salad, combine the onion, pomegranate seeds and any juices, pomegranate molasses and mint. Season to taste and set aside.

4   When the barbecue is ready, lift the steak from the marinade and barbecue for 3-4 minutes on each side. Transfer to a board, season with salt and let rest for 5 minutes while you warm the pitta breads on the barbecue.

5   To serve, thinly slice the steaks and split the pittas in half. Stuff with the rocket followed by the steak and salad, then drizzle over the sauce and serve.

Beer-glazed chicken skewers with succotash

serves 6   prep time 30 minutes + marinating   cook time 40 minutes

   474 kcal per serving

Whether you're hosting a barbecue or Father's Day gathering or just celebrating a run of sunny weather, these sticky skewers served with an all-American side will go down a treat.

6 x 165g skinless chicken breast fillets, diced

FOR THE MARINADE

2 garlic cloves, crushed

125ml stout

75ml soy sauce

75g clear honey

1 teaspoon Dijon mustard

FOR THE SUCCOTASH

250g frozen broad beans

40g low-fat spread

2 onions, diced

2 teaspoons fresh thyme leaves

4 corn on the cob, kernels removed

2 celery sticks, diced

150g green beans, thinly sliced

10g clear honey

3 teaspoons Dijon mustard

2 garlic cloves, crushed

4 tablespoons cider vinegar

2 tablespoons extra-virgin olive oil

Large handful fresh basil, torn

1   To make the marinade, whisk together the garlic, stout, soy sauce, honey and mustard in a bowl. Add the chicken and toss to coat, then cover and put in the fridge until you're ready to cook. If you're using wooden skewers, put them in water to soak – this will stop them burning on the barbecue.

2   Drain the chicken in a sieve set over a pan to catch the marinade. Thread the chicken onto 6 skewers and set aside. Simmer the marinade, stirring, until it has reduced to a quarter of its original quantity. Set aside.

3   Heat the barbecue while you make the succotash. Blanch the broad beans in a pan of boiling water for 1-2 minutes, then drain and pop them out of their skins.

4   Melt the spread in a flameproof casserole set over a medium heat and fry the onions for 6-8 minutes until softened. Stir in the thyme and cook for 2 minutes, then stir in the sweetcorn, celery and green beans. Cook for 5 minutes, then add the broad beans and cook for 2-3 minutes until the broad beans are tender. Transfer to a serving bowl. For the dressing, whisk together the honey, mustard, garlic, vinegar and olive oil, and season to taste. Drizzle over the succotash, add the basil and toss to coat.

5   Barbecue the skewers for 10-12 minutes, turning regularly and brushing with the reduced marinade every few minutes, until charred, sticky and cooked through. Serve with the succotash.

Scallop & leek risotto

serves 6   prep time 10 minutes   cook time 40 minutes

   401 kcal per serving

When you want to pull out all the stops for a special dinner, make this creamy leek and Parma ham risotto topped with pan-fried juicy scallops and perfectly poached baby leeks.

1.9 litres vegetable stock, made with 1½ stock cubes

6 baby leeks

25g low-fat spread

1 onion, diced

3 leeks, white and green parts separated, both finely sliced

2 garlic cloves, crushed

360g Arborio rice

Grated zest and juice of 1 lemon

50g Parmesan, finely grated

6 slices Parma ham, torn into bite-size pieces

18 large scallops (about 15g each), without roe

2 teaspoons olive oil

1   Put the stock into a medium pan, bring to a simmer, then reduce the heat to low. Add the baby leeks to the pan and poach until tender, then lift from the stock and set aside. Keep the stock on the hob while you make the risotto.

2   Melt the spread in a large flameproof casserole over a low heat, add the onion and the white parts of the leeks, and cook for 10 minutes, stirring, until softened. Add the garlic and cook for another 2 minutes.

3   Stir in the rice and increase the heat to medium. Cook, stirring, for 1 minute, then add the stock, 2 ladlefuls at a time. Stir constantly until the rice has absorbed most of the stock, then add another 2 ladlefuls – repeat this process until the rice has been cooking for 15 minutes. Stir in the remaining leeks and continue to cook the risotto until the stock is all absorbed and the rice is creamy and tender – this will take another 10 or so minutes.

4   Stir the lemon zest and juice, grated Parmesan and Parma ham into the risotto. Season to taste, remove from the heat and cover and set aside to rest for 5 minutes.

5   Season both sides of the scallops. Heat the oil in a large frying pan over a high heat. Sear the scallops for 2 minutes on one side, then turn them over and cook for 1 minute on the other side.

6   Divide the risotto between plates, and top each with a single poached leek and three scallops to serve.

Herb-crusted side of salmon

serves 8   **prep time 10 minutes**   **cook time 25 minutes**

  277 kcal per serving

Looking for an impressive centrepiece for a large family meal or a dish that will work well on a buffet table? This herby whole roasted side of salmon tastes as good as it looks.

1kg side of salmon

1 lemon

1 orange

1 tablespoon clear honey

100g fresh ciabatta, roughly torn

1 shallot, roughly chopped

1 garlic clove, roughly chopped

Handful fresh flat-leaf parsley, leaves picked

Handful fresh dill, plus extra sprigs to garnish

25g capers, drained and chopped

Calorie controlled cooking spray

Cook's tip

Serve the salmon with crushed new potatoes (see recipe, page 151).

1   Preheat the oven to 200°C, fan 180°C, gas mark 6. Line a large shallow roasting tin with baking paper and put the salmon on top. Grate the zest from half the lemon and half the orange, then cut the whole lemon and orange into wedges.

2   In a small bowl, mix the lemon and orange zests with the honey, season, then rub over the top of the salmon. If you need to, you can loosen the mixture with a little lemon juice.

3   Put the ciabatta, shallot, garlic, parsley and dill into a food processor and pulse until you have a green crumb. Transfer to a bowl, stir in the chopped capers, then season and gently press the mixture on top of the salmon. Mist all over with cooking spray, then arrange the lemon and orange wedges around the salmon.

4   Roast for 20-25 minutes, until the salmon is cooked through and the crumb is crisp. Carefully transfer the salmon side to a large serving platter or board and serve with the extra dill and the roasted wedges for squeezing over.

Cauliflower wellington

serves 6   **prep time 1 hour 15 minutes + chilling**   **cook time 2 hours**

    314 kcal per serving

A whole roasted cauliflower, smothered in mushroom pâté, wrapped in pastry and baked.

1 small-medium cauliflower

Calorie controlled cooking spray

10g dried porcini mushrooms

1 onion, finely chopped

400g chestnut mushrooms, very finely diced (you could do this in a food processor to save time)

¼ teaspoon ground mace

2 garlic cloves, crushed

1 tablespoon fresh thyme leaves

100g whole cooked chestnuts

320g sheet ready-rolled light puff pastry

1 egg, lightly beaten

25g WW Reduced Fat Grated Mature Cheese

4 tablespoons vegetarian gravy granules (we used Sainsbury's)

1   Preheat the oven to 200°C, fan 180°C, gas mark 6 and put the cauliflower on a baking tray. Mist with cooking spray, season and roast for 55 minutes. Remove from the oven and let cool.

2   Meanwhile, put the dried mushrooms in a heatproof jug with 200ml boiling water and let soak for 10 minutes.

3   Mist a nonstick pan with cooking spray and fry the onion over medium heat for 6-8 minutes. Stir in the chestnut mushrooms and cook for 15 minutes. Add the mace, garlic and thyme, and cook for 2 minutes, then transfer half the mixture to a bowl and the rest to a food processor. Strain the rehydrated mushrooms, reserving the liquid, then add them to the food processor with the chestnuts. Pulse to a purée, then stir it into the remaining mushroom filling. Season and set aside to cool. Press the pâté over the cauliflower to coat. Chill in the fridge for 30 minutes.

4   Roll the pastry out to a thin square. Brush the cauliflower with a little of the egg, then put it in the centre of the pastry, pâté-side down. Bring the pastry up and around the sides, pinching it at the base to seal. Put, seal-side down, onto a baking sheet lined with baking paper and chill in the fridge for 30 minutes.

5   Preheat the oven to 200°C, fan 180°C, gas mark 6. Brush the pastry with a little egg, then bake for 25 minutes. Brush with more egg and press the cheese over the top. Bake for 15 minutes.

6   To make a mushroom gravy, mix the gravy granules with the reserved mushroom soaking liquid and 350ml water in a pan. Heat gently over a medium heat, stirring, until thickened.

7   Cut the wellington into wedges, then serve with the gravy.

Honey & soy-glazed ham

serves 8   prep time 10 minutes + cooling and resting   cook time 2 hours

  283 kcal per serving

A flavourful glazed ham is thoroughly deserving of a place on your menu at celebration buffets and posh picnics. Any leftovers can be served up in breakfasts, lunches and more.

1.4kg unsmoked gammon joint

1 onion, quartered

2 garlic cloves

5 star anise

10 peppercorns

FOR THE HONEY & SOY GLAZE

25g light brown soft sugar

1 tablespoon clear honey

1 tablespoon soy sauce

1 tablespoon Chinese cooking wine (or dry sherry)

¼ teaspoon Chinese 5 spice

Pared zest of 1 orange

1 Roll the gammon joint and tie securely with kitchen string, then transfer to a large, deep pot. Add the onion, garlic, 2 of the star anise and all the peppercorns, then pour over enough cold water to cover the joint. Bring the mixture to the boil, then reduce the heat and simmer for 1 hour 20 minutes, skimming the surface every so often and topping up the water if you need to.

2 Carefully remove the gammon from the cooking liquid and set aside on a board until cool enough to handle. Discard the cooking liquid. Using a small, sharp knife, cut away the string and the skin, taking care not to remove too much fat. Score a diamond pattern into the fat.

3 Preheat the oven to 200°C, fan 180°C, gas mark 6 and line a baking tray with baking paper. Make the glaze: put the brown sugar, honey, soy sauce, cooking wine, Chinese 5 spice and half of the orange zest in a pan and simmer over a medium heat, until the sugar has dissolved and the liquid has reduced. Brush the joint all over with half of the glaze, then stud the fat with the remaining star anise. Transfer to the prepared baking tray and bake for 25-30 minutes, brushing regularly with the remaining glaze, until the joint is sticky and caramelised.

4 Remove from the oven and let rest for at least 30 minutes before carving. Serve topped with the remaining orange zest.

MEMBERS' FAVOURITE
Chocolate celebration cake

serves 14   prep time 20 minutes + cooling   cook time 25 minutes

   267 kcal per serving

A decadent chocolate cake that's easy to make, looks amazing and caters to many dietary requirements? It's easy to see why members flock to this accessible bake.

150g dairy-free spread, plus an extra 1 teaspoon for greasing

150g caster sugar

280g self-raising flour

40g cacao powder, plus an extra 5g for dusting

1 teaspoon baking powder

1 teaspoon bicarbonate of soda

280ml unsweetened almond milk

1 tablespoon white wine vinegar

150g strawberries, hulled and sliced, plus extra halved strawberries to decorate

150g raspberries

FOR THE CHOCOLATE FILLING

120g dairy-free spread

2½ tablespoons cacao powder

3 tablespoons icing sugar

1 Preheat the oven to 190°C, fan 170°C, gas mark 5. Grease 2 x 18cm round cake tins with dairy-free spread and line the bases and sides with baking paper. Put 150g of the spread and all the caster sugar into a large bowl and beat with a hand-held electric whisk for 4-5 minutes, until light and fluffy.

2 In another bowl, combine the flour, cacao powder, baking powder and bicarbonate of soda. Whisk half of the dry ingredients into the spread and sugar mixture, using a hand-held electric whisk. In a large jug, combine the almond milk and vinegar, then whisk half of this mixture into the cake mixture. Repeat with the remaining dry ingredients and almond milk mixture until smooth.

3 Divide the batter between the prepared tins and smooth the surfaces. Bake for 25 minutes, or until a skewer inserted into the centre of the cakes comes out clean. Set aside to cool in the tins for 15 minutes, then release and transfer to a wire rack to cool completely.

4 For the chocolate filling, put the spread in a bowl and sift over the cacao powder and icing sugar. Whisk to combine. To assemble the cake, put one of the sponges on a cake stand and spread the filling over the top. Scatter over half of the sliced strawberries and half of the raspberries, then sandwich with the second sponge. Sift over the remaining cacao powder then top with the remaining berries.

• The unfilled sponges can be frozen, tightly wrapped in clingfilm and then kitchen foil, for up to 2 months.

Raspberry & coconut soufflés

serves 6   **prep time 20 minutes**   **cook time 20 minutes**

    119 kcal per serving

You might think tackling a feather-light soufflé is best left to the professionals, but you'll have no trouble rising to the occasion with this foolproof recipe.

200ml chilled unsweetened coconut drink (we used Alpro)

1 tablespoon cornflour

450g raspberries

4 teaspoons icing sugar

Calorie controlled cooking spray

10g plain flour, for dusting

5 egg whites

80g caster sugar

2 teaspoons desiccated coconut

1   In a small jug, mix 1 tablespoon of the coconut drink with the cornflour to make a smooth paste, then whisk in the rest of the coconut drink. Pour into a pan and set over a medium-low heat, stirring, until it begins to simmer. Cook for 1 minute until thick, then remove from the heat, cover with clingfilm and let cool.

2   Cook the raspberries in a separate pan for 1-2 minutes over a medium heat until they start to release their juices. Transfer to a food processor and blitz to a purée, then press through a sieve to remove the seeds. Set aside 125g to cool for the soufflés, and stir the icing sugar through the remaining purée to make a coulis.

3   Preheat the oven to 220°C, fan 200°C, gas mark 7. Mist 6 x 250ml ramekins with cooking spray, then dust with the flour. Put the ramekins onto a baking tray.

4   Whisk the egg whites in a large bowl until soft peaks form. Beat in the caster sugar, 1 tablespoon at a time, until you have a soft, shiny meringue mixture. In a separate bowl, beat together the coconut mixture and raspberry purée. Gently fold in one-third of the meringue mixture, then fold in the rest in 2 additions.

5   Spoon into the ramekins, flatten the top with a palette knife and run your thumb around the rim to remove any excess mixture so it doesn't stick to the ramekin and hold back the soufflé. Scatter over the coconut, then put the tray on the middle shelf of the oven. Immediately reduce the temperature to 200°C, fan 180°C, gas mark 6 and bake for 11-12 minutes until risen. Serve immediately with the raspberry coulis.

Fig & mascarpone roulade

serves 12   prep time 30 minutes + cooling   cook time 25 minutes

   150 kcal per serving

This springy, marshmallowy, pavlova-like meringue, spread with mascarpone, figs and pistachios and rolled into a log, is an impressive dessert for any occasion.

Calorie controlled cooking spray

4 large egg whites

115g caster sugar

60g light brown soft sugar

1 teaspoon cornflour

1 teaspoon white wine vinegar

1 teaspoon icing sugar, for dusting

FOR THE FILLING

100g low-fat mascarpone

100g reduced-fat crème fraîche

½ teaspoon vanilla extract

25g icing sugar

20g toasted pistachio kernels, roughly chopped

2 fresh figs, chopped

TO DECORATE

5 figs, cut into quarters

20g toasted pistachio kernels, roughly chopped

Handful pomegranate seeds (optional)

Cook's tip
For a neater, more secure roulade, tuck about 4cm of the long edge firmly down into the mascarpone mixture as you start to roll the roulade up.

1 Preheat the oven to 160°C, fan 140°C, gas mark 3. Mist a 25cm x 35cm Swiss roll tin with cooking spray and line with baking paper.

2 To make the roulade, put the egg whites in a large bowl and whisk using a hand-held electric whisk until stiff peaks form. Combine the caster and brown sugars, then whisk into the egg whites, 1 tablespoon at a time, to make a stiff, glossy meringue. Sift over the cornflour, whisk it into the meringue, then whisk in the vinegar. Spoon the meringue evenly into the prepared tin and bake for 25 minutes. Remove from the oven and let cool in the tin for 5 minutes. Dust a large sheet of baking paper with 1 teaspoon of icing sugar. Lift the roulade from the tin and quickly invert it onto the sugar-dusted paper. Peel away the paper, then let the roulade cool completely.

3 To make the filling, put the mascarpone in a bowl and loosen it with a hand-held electric whisk. Add the crème fraîche, vanilla and icing sugar and whisk until smooth and combined. Chill until ready to use.

4 To assemble the roulade, set aside 2 tablespoons of the chilled filling for decoration, then spread the remaining filling over the roulade, leaving a 2.5cm strip along the long edge furthest away from you. Scatter over the pistachios and chopped figs.

5 Starting with the long edge closest to you, and using the paper to help you, roll the roulade so the seam is underneath. Transfer to a platter and spread the reserved filling down the centre of the top. Decorate with the figs, pistachios and pomegranate, if using.

Peanut butter & banana ice-cream sandwiches

makes 12   prep time 20 minutes + freezing

    129 kcal per ice-cream sandwich

Put 480g chopped **frozen bananas** in a blender or food processor and blitz until smooth and creamy. Add ½ teaspoon **vanilla extract** and blitz again, then spoon the mixture into a small baking tin. Smooth over the surface, cover, and freeze for 2-3 hours until solid. Mix 60g **PBFit Powdered Peanut Butter** with 80ml cold water, until combined, then spread over 24 **WW Scottish All Butter Shortbread Thins**. Remove the banana ice cream from the freezer and use a 5cm cookie cutter to stamp out 12 rounds. Working quickly, top half of the shortbread thins with the ice-cream rounds, then sandwich with the remaining shortbread. Grate 20g **dark chocolate** onto a plate, then roll one side of each sandwich into the chocolate. Return to the freezer until ready to serve.

Lemon mousse with ginger crumb

makes 6   prep time 10 minutes + chilling
cook time 10 minutes

    162 kcal per mousse

Separate 3 **eggs**, then lightly whisk the yolks and put them into a small pan with the juice of 5 **lemons** (you'll need 200ml), 140g **caster sugar** and 25g **low-fat spread**. Heat gently over a low heat, whisking to combine, then whisk in 20g **cornflour** and bring the mixture to the boil. Continue to cook, whisking constantly, for 4-5 minutes or until the mixture is smooth and thickened. Remove from the heat and strain into a small bowl. Cover with clingfilm and let cool slightly before chilling in the fridge for 1-2 hours or until completely cold. In a dry, clean bowl, whisk the egg whites until stiff peaks form. Use a metal spoon to gently fold one-third of the egg whites into the chilled lemon curd, then fold in the remaining egg whites. Spoon into small dessert glasses and chill until set. Blitz 1 **ginger nut biscuit** in a mini food processor to coarse crumbs, then sprinkle over the mousse just before serving.

Tropical fruit Charlotte

serves 12   prep time 20 minutes + setting   cook time 5 minutes

   170 kcal per serving

Line an 18cm springform cake tin with clingfilm, allowing some overlap, then line the base with baking paper. Take 175g **sponge finger biscuits** (we used Sainsbury's), then trim the ends of 24 so they stand neatly in the tin. Arrange these around the side of the tin ensuring there are no gaps. Break the remaining sponge fingers into pieces and use these to line the base. To make the filling, soak 6 leaves **gelatine** in cold water for 10 minutes until softened. Meanwhile, put the flesh of 1 **mango** into a mini food processor and blitz to a purée, then scrape into a pan and stir in the zest and juice of 2 **limes** and 60g **caster sugar**.

Warm over a low heat for 5 minutes until the sugar is dissolved. Squeeze excess water from the gelatine and drop into the mango mixture. Stir to dissolve then strain and set aside to cool. Put 600g **0% fat natural Greek yogurt** into a bowl and whisk in the cooled mango until combined. In a separate bowl, whip 200ml **light double cream alternative** to soft peaks then fold into the yogurt mixture. Spoon into the lined tin, then cover and chill for at least 4 hours, or overnight, until set. Release the Charlotte from the tin, discarding the clingfilm and baking paper, then decorate with mango, **kiwi fruit** and **passion fruit**.

Useful information

MEAL PLANS
208 Quick & easy
210 Veggie friendly
212 For the family
214 New to cooking

ZEROPOINT FOODS LISTS
216 Green
218 Blue
219 Purple

INDEXES
220 Recipe index
225 SmartPoints index

Quick & easy

These speedy meals and snacks – ready in 30 minutes or less – are proof that cooking healthy dishes from scratch doesn't have to mean spending hours in the kitchen.

MONDAY 25 16 15

BREAKFAST
Banana, berry & chocolate cereal pots p110

4 3 3

LUNCH
Pesto chicken pasta salad p96

9 7 7

DINNER
Tamarind-glazed salmon with crunchy naked slaw p118

6 1 1

SNACKS/DESSERT
Choc-chip flapjack bites p136

3 3 2

Hot & spicy pulse pot p104

3 2 2

TUESDAY 28 22 16

BREAKFAST
Breakfast tacos with avocado & lime sauce p142

9 5 5

LUNCH
Hot smoked salmon Caesar salad p90

7 5 5

DINNER
Pasta with anchovies & capers p124

8 8 2

SNACKS/DESSERT
Fresh fruit

0 0 0

Banana mocha frappe p86

4 4 4

WEDNESDAY   THURSDAY   FRIDAY

BREAKFAST
Beetroot & blueberry smoothie p86

LUNCH
Cheese & gherkin toastie p28

7 7 7

DINNER
Portobello mushroom 'pizza' p80

6 6 6

SNACKS/DESSERT
Veg crudités with fresh tomato salsa (no oil)

0 0 0

150g 0% fat natural Greek yogurt & fresh fruit

2 0 0

BREAKFAST
Caramelised banana porridge p26

7 7 3

LUNCH
Turkey, apple & smoked Cheddar wraps p88

DINNER
Chilli crab pasta p158

SNACKS/DESSERT
Pumpkin & chia seed bites p102

150g 0% fat natural Greek yogurt & fresh fruit

2 0 0

BREAKFAST
Bloody Mary omelette p26

6 1 1

LUNCH
Chicken tom yum soup p60

3 2 2

DINNER
Balsamic-glazed sausages with roasted garlic mash p34

SNACKS/DESSERT
Frying pan peach crumble p48

Pumpkin & chia seed bites p102

Veggie friendly

If you're a dedicated vegetarian or just enjoy having an occasional meat-free day, these delicious menus will help keep things varied and interesting.

MONDAY 20 18 16   **TUESDAY** 25 15 15

MONDAY

BREAKFAST
Chia & coconut Bircher muesli with blueberry compote p110
4 4 2

LUNCH
Cheese & gherkin toastie p28
7 7 7

DINNER
Veggie cannelloni p124
8 6 6

SNACKS/DESSERT
Frozen yogurt-coated blueberries p136
1 1 1

Veg crudités with fresh tomato salsa (no oil)
0 0 0

TUESDAY

BREAKFAST
Banana, berry & chocolate cereal pots p110
4 3 3

LUNCH
Bloody Mary omelette p26
6 1 1

DINNER
Vegan agedashi tofu p116
5 2 2

SNACKS/DESSERT
Raspberry blondies p103
5 4 4

Seed crackers with artichoke dip p134
5 5 5

| **WEDNESDAY** 20 19 16 | **THURSDAY** 26 19 16 | **FRIDAY** 29 22 16 |

BREAKFAST
Baked oat waffles p24

 4 4 1

LUNCH
Speedy veggie pizza p74

8 8 8

DINNER
Barbecued miso aubergines p184

4 4 4

SNACKS/DESSERT
Apple pie cookies p104

4 3 3

Veg crudités with fresh tomato salsa (no oil)

0 0 0

BREAKFAST
Peach & almond baked oats p111

8 5 2

LUNCH
Italian-style pesto salad p90

6 6 6

DINNER
'Creamy' vegetable pasanda with mini naan p76

8 8 8

SNACKS/DESSERT
Spicy roasted chickpeas p132

2 0 0

150g 0% fat natural Greek yogurt & fresh fruit

2 0 0

BREAKFAST
Breakfast tacos with avocado & lime sauce p142

9 5 5

LUNCH
Spring veg spanakopita p92

10 8 8

DINNER
Pulled mushroom chilli with baked potato mash p40

7 6 1

SNACKS/DESSERT
Pumpkin & chia seed bites p102

2 2 1

Frozen chocolate & raspberry bark p137

1 1 1

For the family

Cook once and keep everyone happy with dishes the whole family will enjoy. If you like, add some extra sides and snacks for the other family members.

MONDAY   27 23 15

TUESDAY   24 20 16

BREAKFAST
Roasted strawberry & almond overnight oats p87
   6 6 3

LUNCH
Turkey, apple & smoked Cheddar wraps p88
   6 6 6

DINNER
Fish pie potato skins p36
   11 9 4

SNACKS/DESSERT
Spring onion & bacon mini muffins p105
   2 2 2

150g 0% fat natural Greek yogurt & fresh fruit
   2 0 0

BREAKFAST
Caramelised banana porridge p26
   7 7 3

LUNCH
Roasted cauliflower, ham & mustard frittata p98
  4 1 1

DINNER
Turkey meatball sliders p154
   7 6 6

SNACKS/DESSERT
Chocolate financiers p172
  6 6 6

Veg crudités with fresh tomato salsa (no oil)
   0 0 0

WEDNESDAY 27 20 16   THURSDAY 20 18 16   FRIDAY 29 23 16

WEDNESDAY

BREAKFAST
Hotdog hash p142

9   7   4

LUNCH
Speedy veggie pizza p74

8   8   8

DINNER
Spanish chicken & butter bean bravas p122

4   0   0

SNACKS/DESSERT
Apple pie cookies p104

4   3   3

Pumpkin & chia seed bites p102

2   2   1

THURSDAY

BREAKFAST
Banana, berry & chocolate cereal pots p110

4   3   3

LUNCH
Turkey & leek bake p30

10   9   9

DINNER
Warm courgette pasta salad p125

6   6   4

SNACKS/DESSERT
Fresh fruit

0   0   0

Veg crudités with fresh tomato salsa (no oil)

0   0   0

FRIDAY

BREAKFAST
Homemade beans on toast p140

7   4   4

LUNCH
Sesame chicken salad p91

3   2   2

DINNER
Sweet chilli fish & chips traybake p68

10   8   3

SNACKS/DESSERT
Peanut butter & banana ice-cream sandwiches p204

3   3   3

2 x PBJ granola cups p102

6   6   4

New to cooking

Anyone can make these easy-to-master recipes and be on their way to healthy-eating success. You'll gain kitchen confidence – and a week of tasty meals.

| MONDAY | 24 19 13 | TUESDAY | 23 22 16 |

BREAKFAST
Homemade granola with fruit & yogurt p84
 7 6 4

LUNCH
Tapenade tuna salad p120
 6 4 4

DINNER
Spring chicken traybake p114
 6 4 0

SNACKS/DESSERT
Peanut butter & banana ice-cream sandwiches p204
 3 3 3

Spring onion & bacon mini muffins p105
 2 2 2

BREAKFAST
Beetroot & blueberry smoothie p86
 3 3 3

LUNCH
Keralan chicken curry soup p31
 10 9 7

DINNER
Harissa steak salad p126
 7 7 4

SNACKS/DESSERT
Frozen chocolate & raspberry bark p137
 1 1 1

Pumpkin & chia seed bites p102
 2 2 1

WEDNESDAY 22 18 15   THURSDAY 30 17 15   FRIDAY 22 16 15

BREAKFAST
Roasted strawberry & almond overnight oats p87
  6 6 3

LUNCH
Turkey, apple & smoked Cheddar wraps p88
 6 6 6

DINNER
Spanish chicken & butter bean bravas p122
 4 0 0

SNACKS/DESSERT
Banana mocha frappe p86
 4 4 4

Spring onion & bacon mini muffins p105
 2 2 2

BREAKFAST
Bloody Mary omelette p26
 6 1 1

LUNCH
Roasted cauliflower, ham & mustard frittata p98
 4 1 1

DINNER
Balsamic-glazed sausages with roasted garlic mash p34
 11 6 6

SNACKS/DESSERT
Carrot cake flapjacks p100
 3 3 2

Frying pan peach crumble p48
6 6 5

BREAKFAST
Scrambled eggs with mushrooms & smoked trout p108
 6 1 1

LUNCH
Chicken tom yum soup p60
 3 2 2

DINNER
Korean veggie stir-fry with crispy rice p80
 9 9 9

SNACKS/DESSERT
Frozen yogurt-coated blueberries p136
 1 1 1

Carrot cake flapjacks p100
 3 3 2

Your ZeroPoint foods list

Green

You can enjoy more than 100 fresh fruits and non-starchy vegetables – mix and match them with all your favourite foods, without having to focus on measuring, weighing or tracking them.

FRUITS
Apples
Apricots (fresh)
Bananas
Blackberries
Blueberries
Cantaloupe
melons
Cherries
Clementines
Cranberries (fresh)
Dragon fruits
Figs (fresh)
Frozen
mixed berries
(unsweetened)
Fruit cocktail
(unsweetened)
Grapefruits
Grapes
Guava
Honeydew melons
Kiwi fruits
Kumquats
Lemons
Limes
Mangoes
Nectarines
Oranges
Papayas
Peaches
Pears
Persimmons
Pineapples
Plums
Pomegranates

Pomelo
Raspberries
Star fruit
Strawberries
Tangerines
Watermelons

**VEGETABLES
(NON-STARCHY)
& HERBS**
Acorn squash
Artichoke hearts
(no oil)
Artichokes
Asparagus
Aubergines
Baby corn
Basil
Beetroot
Broccoli
Brussels sprouts
Butternut squash
Cabbage
Carrots
Cauliflower
Cauliflower rice
Celery
Chives
Coriander
Courgettes
Cucumber
Endive
Fennel
Frozen stir-fry
vegetables
(no sauce)

Garlic
Ginger
Green beans
Kale
Kohlrabi
Leeks
Lettuce
(all types)
Mint
Mixed greens
Mushrooms
Nori (seaweed)
Okra
Onions
Oregano
Pak choi
Parsley
Pea shoots
Peppers
Pickles
(unsweetened)
Pumpkin
Radishes
Rocket
Rosemary
Shallots
Spaghetti squash
Spinach
Spring onions
Swiss chard
Tarragon
Thyme
Tomatoes
Turnips
Water chestnuts

Find out more
You'll discover a full version of the ZeroPoint foods lists for Green, Blue and Purple on the WW website or the WW app.

Your ZeroPoint foods list

More than 200 foods, including most fruits, non-starchy veg, eggs, skinless chicken and turkey breast fillets, fish and shellfish, beans and legumes, tofu and fat-free plain yogurt.

BEANS & LEGUMES
Black beans
Black-eyed peas
Cannellini beans
Chickpeas
Kidney beans
Lentils
Lima beans
Pinto beans
Refried beans
(fat-free, tinned)
Soya beans

CHICKEN & TURKEY
Chicken
breast mince
Skinless chicken
breast fillets
Skinless turkey
breast fillets
Turkey breast
mince

EGGS
Eggs (all types)

FAT-FREE YOGURT & SOYA
Greek yogurt
(plain, fat-free)
Plain yogurt
(fat-free)
Quark
(plain, fat-free)
Soya yogurt
(plain)

FISH & SHELLFISH
Anchovies
(in water)
Carp
Catfish
Caviar

Clams
Cod
Crabmeat (lump)
Crayfish
Cuttlefish
Eel
Fish roe
Flounder
Grouper
Haddock
Halibut
Herring
Lobster
Mahi mahi
Monkfish
Mussels
Octopus
Orange roughy
Oysters
Perch
Pike
Pollock
Pompano
Prawns
Salmon
Sardines (tinned,
in water or brine)
Sashimi
Scallops
Sea bass
Sea cucumber
Sea urchin
Shrimp
Smoked
haddock
Smoked
mackerel
Smoked salmon
Smoked
sturgeon
Smoked trout
Smoked
whitefish
Snapper
Sole
Squid

Sturgeon
Swordfish
Tilapia
Trout
Tuna
Turbot
White fish

FRUITS
Apples
Apricots (fresh)
Bananas
Blackberries
Blueberries
Cantaloupe
melons
Cherries
Clementines
Cranberries
(fresh)
Dragon fruits
Figs (fresh)
Frozen
mixed berries
(unsweetened)
Fruit cocktail
(unsweetened)
Grapefruits
Grapes
Guava
Honeydew
melons
Kiwi fruits
Kumquats
Lemons
Limes
Mangoes
Nectarines
Oranges
Papayas
Peaches
Pears
Persimmons
Pineapples
Plums
Pomegranates

Pomelo
Raspberries
Star fruit
Strawberries
Tangerines
Watermelons

QUORN, TOFU AND TEMPEH
Quorn
(plain, all types)
Tempeh
(plain, all types)
Tofu (plain,
all types)

VEGETABLES (NON-STARCHY) & HERBS
Acorn squash
Artichoke hearts
(no oil)
Artichokes
Asparagus
Aubergines
Baby corn
Bamboo shoots
Basil
Bean sprouts
Beetroot
Broad beans
Broccoli
Brussels sprouts
Butternut
squash
Cabbage
(all types)
Carrots
Cauliflower
Cauliflower rice
Celery
Chives
Coriander
Corn on the cob
Courgettes
Cucumber

Edamame
Endive
Fennel
Garlic
Ginger
Green beans
Kale
Kohlrabi
Leeks
Lettuce
(all types)
Mint
Mixed greens
Mushrooms
Nori (seaweed)
Okra
Onions
Oregano
Pak choi
Parsley
Parsnips
Peas

Pea shoots
Peppers
Pickles
(unsweetened)
Pumpkin
Radishes
Rocket
Rosemary
Shallots
Spring onions
Spaghetti
squash
Spinach
Sweetcorn
Swiss chard
Tarragon
Thyme
Tomatoes
Turnips
Water chestnuts

Your ZeroPoint foods list

Purple

There are more than 300 zero heroes to turn to, including everything you'll find on the Green and Blue lists, as well as potatoes, wholewheat pasta and grains, and more.

BEANS & LEGUMES
Aduki beans
Black bean pasta
Black beans
Black-eyed peas
Cannellini beans
Chickpea pasta
Chickpeas
Kidney beans
Lentil pasta
Lentils
Pea pasta
Pinto beans
Refried beans
(tinned, fat-free)
Soya beans
Split peas

CHICKEN & TURKEY
Skinless
chicken breast
Skinless
turkey breast
Turkey breast
mince

DAIRY & SOYA
Cottage cheese
(plain, fat-free)
Greek yogurt
(plain, fat-free)
Plain yogurt
(fat-free)
Quark (plain,
fat-free)
Soya yogurt
(plain)

EGGS
Eggs (all types)

FISH & SHELLFISH
Anchovies

Carp
Catfish
Caviar
Clams
Cod
Crabmeat (lump)
Cuttlefish
Eel
Fish roe
Flounder
Grouper
Haddock
Halibut
Herring
Lobster
Monkfish
Mussels
Octopus
Orange roughy
Oysters
Perch
Pike
Pollock
Prawns
Salmon
Sardines (tinned,
in water or brine)
Sashimi
Scallops
Sea bass
Sea urchin
Shrimp
Smelt
Smoked haddock
Smoked
mackerel
Smoked salmon
Smoked trout
Snapper
Sole
Squid
Sturgeon
Swordfish
Tilapia
Trout
Tuna

Tuna (tinned,
in water or brine)
Turbot
Whitefish

FRUITS
Apples
Apricots (fresh)
Bananas
Blackberries
Blueberries
Cantaloupe
melons
Cherries
Clementines
Cranberries
(fresh)
Dragon fruits
Figs (fresh)
Frozen
mixed berries,
(unsweetened)
Fruit cocktail
(unsweetened)
Grapefruit
Grapes
Guava
Honeydew
melons
Kiwi fruits
Kumquats
Lemons
Limes
Mangoes
Nectarines
Oranges
Papayas
Peaches
Pears
Persimmons
Pineapples
Plums
Pomegranates
Pomelo
Raspberries
Star fruit

Strawberries
Tangerines
Watermelon

PASTA, RICE & GRAINS
Amaranth
Barley
Brown rice
Brown rice
noodles
Brown rice pasta
Brown rice
quinoa blend
Buckwheat
Bulgur wheat
Edamame pasta
Farro
Freekeh
Kamut
Kasha
Millet
Oats
Popcorn (air-
popped, plain)
Quinoa
Quinoa pasta
Red quinoa
Rolled oats
Rye
Soba noodles,
(100%
buckwheat)
Spelt
Teff
Thai brown rice
Tricolour quinoa
Wheatberries
Wholewheat
couscous
Wholewheat
pasta
Wholewheat
sorghum
Wild rice
Wild rice (brown)

QUORN, TOFU AND TEMPEH
Quorn (plain)
Silken tofu
Smoked tofu
Tempeh (plain)
Tofu (plain)

VEGETABLES (NON-STARCHY) & HERBS
Acorn squash
Alfalfa sprouts
Artichoke
hearts (no oil)
Artichokes
Asparagus
Baby corn
Bamboo shoots
Basil
Beansprouts
Beetroot
Broad beans
Broccoli
Brussels sprouts
Butternut
squash
Cabbage
Carrots
Cauliflower
Celery
Chives
Coriander
Courgettes
Cucumber
Edamame
Endive
Fennel
Frozen stir-fry
veg (no sauce)
Garlic
Ginger
Green beans
Kale
Kohlrabi
Leeks

Lettuce
Mint
Mushrooms
Nori (seaweed)
Okra
Onions
Oregano
Parsley
Parsnips
Peas
Pea shoots
Peppers
Pickles
(unsweetened)
Pumpkin
Radishes
Rosemary
Salsa (fresh,
no oil)
Sauerkraut
Shallots
Spinach
Spring onions
Swiss chard
Tarragon
Thyme
Tomatoes
Turnips
Water chestnuts

VEGETABLES (STARCHY)
Baby potatoes
Cassava
Corn
Corn (tinned)
Mashed
potatoes (plain)
Mashed sweet
potatoes (plain)
New potatoes
Potatoes
Sweet potatoes
Taro
Yams
Yuca

Recipe index

ALMONDS
Apple & blackberry sponge
puddings 49
Chocolate financiers 172
'Creamy' vegetable pasanda 76
Homemade granola 84
Roasted strawberry &
almond overnight oats 87

ANCHOVIES
Hot smoked salmon Caesar salad 90
Pasta with anchovies & capers 124
Roasted lamb with salsa
verde beans 148

APPLES
Apple & blackberry sponge
puddings 49
Apple pie cookies 104
Chia & coconut Bircher muesli
with blueberry compote 110
Roast pork with onion gravy 146
Roasted apples with
cinder toffee 48
Sticky pudding with apple crisps 168
Turkey, apple & smoked
Cheddar wraps 88
Apricot tarte tatin 170

ARTICHOKES
Seed crackers with artichoke dip 134

ASPARAGUS
Roasted cauliflower, ham
& mustard frittata 98
Spring chicken traybake 114
Spring vegetable spanakopita 92
Veggie cannelloni 124
Zesty asparagus, beans & peas 150

AUBERGINES
Aubergine & lentil puttanesca
with Parma-wrapped cod 164
Barbecued miso aubergines 184
Italian-style pesto salad 90
Soy salmon with sweet & sour
aubergines 160
Veggie katsu rice bowl 78

AVOCADO
Breakfast tacos with
avocado & lime sauce 142

BACON
Herbed crushed new potatoes 151
Homemade beans on toast 140
Pork cassoulet 38
Spring onion & bacon
mini muffins 105
Turkey & leek bake 30
Baked oat waffles 24
Baked rice pudding 46
Balsamic beetroot & ricotta toasts 179
Balsamic-glazed sausages
with roasted garlic mash 34

BANANAS
Baked oat waffles 24
Banana, berry & chocolate
cereal pots 110
Banana mocha frappe 86
Caramelised banana porridge 26
Peanut butter & banana
ice-cream sandwiches 204
Barbecued miso aubergines 184

BEANS
Balsamic-glazed sausages with
roasted garlic mash 34
Beer-glazed chicken skewers
with succotash 188
Homemade beans on toast 140
Lettuce cup beef tacos
with jalapeño sauce 62
Pork cassoulet 38
Raspberry blondies 103
Roasted lamb with salsa
verde beans 148
Spanish chicken & butter
bean bravas 122
Sriracha pork chops with
celeriac & butter bean mash 166

BEEF
Beef bulgogi noodle stir-fry 55
Griddled rump steak with
chips & mustard 'mayo' 182
Harissa steak salad 126
Lettuce cup beef tacos
with jalapeño sauce 62
Melt-in-the-middle burgers 52
Steak & pepper quesadillas 112
Turkish steak pittas 186
Beer-glazed chicken skewers
with succotash 188

BEETROOT
Balsamic beetroot &
ricotta toasts 179
Beetroot & blueberry smoothie 86

BISCUITS
Apple pie cookies 104
Lemon mousse with
ginger crumb 204
Frying pan peach crumble 48
Peanut butter & banana
ice-cream sandwiches 204
Seed crackers with artichoke dip 134
Tropical fruit Charlotte 205

BLACKBERRIES
Apple & blackberry sponge
puddings 49
Bloody Mary omelette 26

BLUEBERRIES
Baked oat waffles 24
Banana, berry & chocolate
cereal pots 110
Beetroot & blueberry smoothie 86
Chia & coconut Bircher
muesli with blueberry compote 110
Frozen yogurt-coated blueberries 136
Breakfast rolls 27
Breakfast tacos with
avocado & lime sauce 142

BROCCOLI
Cheese & onion pie with
minted greens 152
Harissa steak salad 126
Pesto chicken pasta salad 96
Roasted cauliflower, ham
& mustard frittata 98
Sweet chilli fish & chips traybake 68
Teriyaki cod with soba
noodle salad 72

BRUSSELS SPROUTS
Creamed greens 150

Crispy gnocchi with ham
hock & shredded greens 162
Kung pao turkey stir-fry 54
Sticky spiced chicken &
butternut squash traybake 128

BURGERS
Melt-in-the-middle burgers 52
Turkey meatball sliders 154

BUTTERNUT SQUASH
Griddled rump steak with
chips & mustard 'mayo' 182
Sticky spiced chicken &
butternut squash traybake 128

CABBAGE
Creamed greens 150
Crispy gnocchi with ham
hock & shredded greens 162
Tamarind-glazed salmon
with crunchy naked slaw 118

CAKES
Chocolate celebration cake 198
Chocolate financiers 172
Coffee & walnut angel cake 172
Fig & mascarpone roulade 202

CAPERS
Aubergine & lentil puttanesca
with Parma-wrapped cod 164
Herb-crusted side of salmon 192
Hot smoked salmon Caesar salad 90
Pasta with anchovies & capers 124
Roasted lamb with salsa
verde beans 148
Caramelised banana porridge 26
Carrot cake flapjacks 100

CAULIFLOWER
Cauliflower wellington 194
Cauliflower 'wings' with
chickpea dip 180
'Creamy' vegetable pasanda 76
Indonesian-style coconut
prawns with cauliflower rice 58
Roasted cauliflower, ham
& mustard frittata 98

CELERIAC
Celeriac & smoked haddock gratin 30
Sriracha pork chops with
celeriac & butter bean mash 166

CHIA SEEDS
Chia & coconut Bircher muesli
with blueberry compote 110
Pumpkin & chia seed bites 102
Seed crackers with artichoke dip 134

CHICKEN
Beer-glazed chicken skewers
with succotash 188
Chicken & mushroom stroganoff 32
Chicken tom yum soup 60
Keralan chicken curry soup 31
Pesto chicken pasta salad 96
Pulled chicken bao buns 156
Roast chicken dinner traybake 42
Sesame chicken salad 91
Shawarma chicken with
fattoush salad 56
Spanish chicken & butter
bean bravas 122
Spring chicken traybake 114

Sticky spiced chicken
& butternut squash traybake 128

CHICKPEAS
Cauliflower 'wings' with
chickpea dip 180
Greek-style pork souvlaki with
tomato rice salad 66
Hot & spicy pulse pot 104
Spicy roasted chickpeas 132
Sweet potato & chickpea rolls 178
Choc-chip flapjack bites 136

CHOCOLATE
Choc-chip flapjack bites 136
Chocolate celebration cake 198
Chocolate financiers 172
Frozen chocolate &
raspberry bark 137
Peanut butter & banana
ice-cream sandwiches 204
Raspberry blondies 103

CHORIZO
Smoky salmon &
chorizo skewers 184

COCKTAILS
Cranberry & thyme gin cocktail 176

COCONUT
Chia & coconut Bircher
muesli with blueberry compote 110
'Creamy' vegetable pasanda 76
Indonesian-style coconut
prawns with cauliflower rice 58
Keralan chicken curry soup 31
Raspberry & coconut soufflés 200
Veggie katsu rice bowl 78

COFFEE
Banana mocha frappe 86
Coffee & walnut angel cake 172

CORN
Beer-glazed chicken skewers
with succotash 188
Korean veggie stir-fry
with crispy rice 80

COURGETTES
Courgette bites with feta dip 178
Indonesian-style coconut
prawns with cauliflower rice 58
Italian-style pesto salad 90
Veggie cannelloni 124
Warm courgette pasta salad 125

COUSCOUS
Turkish-style lamb skewers
with couscous 70

CRAB
Chilli crab pasta 158
Cranberry & thyme gin cocktail 176
Creamed greens 150
'Creamy' vegetable pasanda 76
Crispy gnocchi with ham
hock & shredded greens 162

CUCUMBER
Greek-style pork souvlaki with
tomato rice salad 66
Sesame chicken salad 91
Sesame prawns with sriracha 176
Shawarma chicken with
fattoush salad 56
Tapenade tuna salad 120

Turkish-style lamb
skewers with couscous 70

CURRY
'Creamy' vegetable pasanda 76
Indonesian-style coconut
prawns with cauliflower rice 58
Keralan chicken curry soup 31
Veggie katsu rice bowl 78

DATES
Pumpkin & chia seed bites 102

EGGS
Bloody Mary omelette 26
Breakfast rolls 27
Breakfast tacos with
avocado & lime sauce 142
Hot smoked salmon Caesar
salad 90
Hotdog hash 142
Pea & Parma ham quiche 94
Raspberry & coconut soufflés 200
Roasted cauliflower, ham
& mustard frittata 98
Scrambled eggs with
mushrooms & smoked trout 108
Smoked salmon sharing rösti 143

Fig & mascarpone roulade 202

FISH
Aubergine & lentil puttanesca
with Parma-wrapped cod 164
Celeriac & smoked
haddock gratin 30
Fish pie potato skins 36
Herb-crusted side of salmon 192
Hot smoked salmon Caesar salad 90
Scrambled eggs with
mushrooms & smoked trout 108
Smoky salmon &
chorizo skewers 184
Soy salmon with sweet
& sour aubergines 160
Sweet chilli fish & chips traybake 68
Tamarind-glazed salmon with
crunchy naked slaw 118
Tapenade tuna salad 120

Teriyaki cod with soba
noodle salad 72
Vietnamese turmeric fish 64

FLAPJACKS
Carrot cake flapjacks 100
Choc-chip flapjack bites 136
French onion hotdogs 54
Frozen chocolate & raspberry bark 137
Frozen yogurt-coated blueberries 136
Frying pan peach crumble 48

GIN
Cranberry & thyme gin cocktail 176

GNOCCHI
Crispy gnocchi with ham
hock & shredded greens 162

GRANOLA
Homemade granola 84
PBJ granola cups 102
Greek-style pork souvlaki
with tomato rice salad 66

HAM
Aubergine & lentil puttanesca
with Parma-wrapped cod 164
Breakfast rolls 27
Crispy gnocchi with ham
hock & shredded greens 162
Honey & soy-glazed ham 196
Pea & Parma ham quiche 94
Roasted cauliflower, ham
& mustard frittata 98
Scallop & leek risotto 190
Harissa steak salad 126
Herb-crusted side of salmon 192
Herbed crushed new potatoes 151
Homemade beans on toast 140
Homemade granola 84
Honey & soy-glazed ham 196
Hot & spicy pulse pot 104
Hot smoked salmon Caesar salad 90

Recipe index

HOTDOGS
French onion hotdogs 54
Hotdog hash 142

ICE CREAM
Peanut butter & banana
ice-cream sandwiches 204
Roasted apples with cinder toffee 48
Indonesian-style coconut
prawns with cauliflower rice 58
Italian-style pesto salad 90

KALE
Celeriac & smoked
haddock gratin 30
Creamed greens 150
Keralan chicken curry soup 31
Veggie katsu rice bowl 78
Keralan chicken curry soup 31
Korean veggie stir-fry with
crispy rice 80
Kung pao turkey stir-fry 54

LAMB
Roasted lamb with salsa
verde beans 148
Turkish-style lamb skewers
with couscous 70

LEEKS
Crispy gnocchi with ham
hock & shredded greens 162
Fish pie potato skins 36
Scallop & leek risotto 190
Spring vegetable spanakopita 92
Turkey & leek bake 30
Lemon mousse with ginger crumb 204

LENTILS
Aubergine & lentil puttanesca
with Parma-wrapped cod 164
Pulled mushroom chilli with
baked potato mash 40
Spiced turkey mujadarra 130
Lettuce cup beef tacos with
jalapeño sauce 62

Melt-in-the-middle burgers 52
MISO PASTE
Barbecued miso aubergines 184
MUFFINS
Spring onion & bacon
mini muffins 105
MUSHROOMS
Breakfast rolls 27
Cauliflower wellington 194
Chicken & mushroom
stroganoff 32
Chicken tom yum soup 60
Korean veggie stir-fry
with crispy rice 80
Oven-baked pumpkin
& porcini risotto 44
Portobello mushroom 'pizza' 80
Pulled mushroom chilli with
baked potato mash 40
Scrambled eggs with
mushrooms & smoked trout 108
Speedy veggie pizza 74
Vegan agedashi tofu 116

NOODLES
Beef bulgogi noodle stir-fry 55
Teriyaki cod with soba
noodle salad 72
Vietnamese turmeric fish 64

OATS
Apple pie cookies 104
Baked oat waffles 24
Caramelised banana porridge 26
Chia & coconut Bircher
muesli with blueberry compote 110
Choc-chip flapjack bites 136
Frying pan peach crumble 48
Homemade granola 84
PBJ granola cups 102
Peach & almond baked oats 111
Pumpkin & chia seed bites 102
Roasted strawberry &
almond overnight oats 87

OMELETTE
Bloody Mary omelette 26
Oven-baked pumpkin
& porcini risotto 44

PANCAKES
Pumpkin pie pancakes 144

PASTA
Chilli crab pasta 158
Pasta with anchovies & capers 124
Pesto chicken pasta salad 96
Veggie cannelloni 124
Warm courgette pasta salad 125

PASTRY
Apricot tarte tatin 170
Cauliflower wellington 194
Spring vegetable spanakopita 92
Sweet potato & chickpea rolls 178
PBJ granola cups 102

PEACHES
Frying pan peach crumble 48
Peach & almond baked oats 111

PEANUT BUTTER
PBJ granola cups 102
Peanut butter & banana
ice-cream sandwiches 204

PEAS
Cheese & onion pie with
minted greens 152
Pea & Parma ham quiche 94
Roast chicken dinner traybake 42
Spring vegetable spanakopita 92
Teriyaki cod with soba
noodle salad 72
Veggie cannelloni 124
Zesty asparagus,
beans & peas 150

PESTO
Italian-style pesto salad 90
Pesto chicken pasta salad 96

PIZZA
Portobello mushroom 'pizza' 80
Speedy veggie pizza 74

POMEGRANATE
Fig & mascarpone roulade 202
Turkish steak pittas 186
Turkish-style lamb skewers
with couscous 70

PORK
Greek-style pork souvlaki
with tomato rice salad 66
Pork cassoulet 38
Roast pork with onion gravy 146
Sriracha pork chops with
celeriac & butter bean mash 166

PORRIDGE
Caramelised banana porridge 26
Portobello mushroom 'pizza' 80

POTATOES
Cheese & onion pie with
minted greens 152
Fish pie potato skins 36
Griddled rump steak with
chips & mustard 'mayo' 182
Harissa steak salad 126
Herbed crushed new potatoes 151
Hotdog hash 142
Keralan chicken curry soup 31
Pulled mushroom chilli
with baked potato mash 40
Roast chicken dinner traybake 42
Roast pork with onion gravy 146
Smoked salmon sharing rösti 143
Spring chicken traybake 114

PRAWNS
Indonesian-style coconut
prawns with cauliflower rice 58
Sesame prawns with sriracha 176
Pulled chicken bao buns 156
Pulled mushroom chilli with
baked potato mash 40

PUMPKIN
Hot & spicy pulse pot 104
Oven-baked pumpkin
& porcini risotto 44
Pumpkin & chia seed bites 102
Pumpkin pie pancakes 144

QUICHE
Pea & Parma ham quiche 94

QUINOA
Veggie katsu rice bowl 78

RADISHES
Shawarma chicken with
fattoush salad 56
Spring chicken traybake 114

RAISINS
Warm courgette pasta salad 125

RASPBERRIES
Chocolate celebration cake 198
Frozen chocolate
& raspberry bark 137
Raspberry & coconut soufflés 200
Raspberry blondies 103

RICE
Baked rice pudding 46
Chicken & mushroom stroganoff 32
Greek-style pork souvlaki
with tomato rice salad 66
Keralan chicken curry soup 31
Korean veggie stir-fry with
crispy rice 80
Oven-baked pumpkin
& porcini risotto 44
Scallop & leek risotto 190

Soy salmon with sweet
& sour aubergines 160
Spiced turkey mujadarra 130
Sticky spiced chicken
& butternut squash traybake 128
Veggie katsu rice bowl 78

RISOTTO
Oven-baked pumpkin
& porcini risotto 44
Scallop & leek risotto 190
Roast chicken dinner traybake 42
Roast pork with onion gravy 146
Roasted apples with cinder toffee 48
Roasted cauliflower, ham
& mustard frittata 98
Roasted lamb with salsa
verde beans 148
Roasted strawberry & almond
overnight oats 87

SALAD
Greek-style pork souvlaki with
tomato rice salad 66
Hot smoked salmon Caesar salad 90
Italian-style pesto salad 90
Pesto chicken pasta salad 96
Sesame chicken salad 91
Shawarma chicken with
fattoush salad 56
Tamarind-glazed salmon
with crunchy naked slaw 118
Tapenade tuna salad 120
Teriyaki cod with soba
noodle salad 72
Turkish-style lamb skewers
with couscous 70
Warm courgette pasta salad 125

SALMON
Herb-crusted side of salmon 192
Hot smoked salmon Caesar salad 90
Smoked salmon sharing rösti 143
Smoky salmon
& chorizo skewers 184
Soy salmon with sweet
& sour aubergines 160
Tamarind-glazed salmon with
crunchy naked slaw 118

SAUSAGES
Balsamic-glazed sausages
with roasted garlic mash 34
French onion hotdogs 54
Scallop & leek risotto 190
Scrambled eggs with
mushrooms & smoked trout 108
Seed crackers with artichoke dip 134
Sesame chicken salad 91
Sesame prawns with sriracha 176

SESAME SEEDS
Beef bulgogi noodle stir-fry 55
Pumpkin & chia seed bites 102
Seed crackers with artichoke dip 134
Sesame chicken salad 91
Sesame prawns with sriracha 176
Sweet chilli fish & chips traybake 68
Teriyaki cod with soba
noodle salad 72

SHALLOTS
Cheese & gherkin toastie 28

Herb-crusted side of salmon 192
Lettuce cup beef tacos
with jalapeño sauce 62
Oven-baked pumpkin
& porcini risotto 44
Pea & Parma ham quiche 94
Pork cassoulet 38
Seed crackers with artichoke dip 134
Spanish chicken & butter
bean bravas 122
Veggie katsu rice bowl 78
Shawarma chicken with
fattoush salad 56
Smoked salmon sharing rösti 143
Smoky salmon & chorizo skewers 184

SMOOTHIES
Beetroot & blueberry smoothie 86

SOUP
Chicken tom yum soup 60
Keralan chicken curry soup 31
Soy salmon with sweet & sour
aubergines 160
Spanish chicken & butter
bean bravas 122
Speedy veggie pizza 74
Spiced turkey mujadarra 130
Spicy roasted chickpeas 132
Spring chicken traybake 114

SPRING ONIONS
Barbecued miso aubergines 184
Courgette bites with feta dip 178
Hotdog hash 142
Korean veggie stir-fry with
crispy rice 80
Kung pao turkey stir-fry 54
Pulled chicken bao buns 156
Sesame chicken salad 91
Soy salmon with sweet & sour
aubergines 160
Speedy veggie pizza 74
Spring chicken traybake 114
Spring onion & bacon
mini muffins 105
Sticky spiced chicken
& butternut squash traybake 128
Sweet chilli fish & chips traybake 68
Tamarind-glazed salmon with
crunchy naked slaw 118
Teriyaki cod with soba
noodle salad 72
Veggie cannelloni 124
Spring vegetable spanakopita 92
Sriracha pork chops with
celeriac & butter bean mash 166
Steak & pepper quesadillas 112
Sticky pudding with apple crisps 168
Sticky spiced chicken
& butternut squash traybake 128

STIR-FRIES
Korean veggie stir-fry
with crispy rice 80
Kung pao turkey stir-fry 54

STRAWBERRIES
Banana, berry & chocolate
cereal pots 110
Chocolate celebration cake 198
Roasted strawberry & almond
overnight oats 87

Sweet chilli fish & chips traybake 68
SWEET POTATOES
Griddled rump steak with
chips & mustard 'mayo' 182
Sweet chilli fish & chips traybake 68
Sweet potato & chickpea rolls 178

TACOS
Breakfast tacos with avocado
& lime sauce 142
Lettuce cup beef tacos
with jalapeño sauce 62
Tamarind-glazed salmon
with crunchy naked slaw 118
Tapenade tuna salad 120
Teriyaki cod with soba noodle salad 72

TOFU
Vegan agedashi tofu 116

TRAYBAKES
Roast chicken dinner traybake 42
Spring chicken traybake 114
Sticky spiced chicken
& butternut squash traybake 128
Sweet chilli fish & chips traybake 68
Tropical fruit Charlotte 205

TUNA
Tapenade tuna salad 120

TURKEY
Kung pao turkey stir-fry 54
Spiced turkey mujadarra 130
Turkey & leek bake 30
Turkey, apple & smoked
Cheddar wraps 88
Turkey meatball sliders 154
Turkish steak pittas 186
Turkish-style lamb skewers
with couscous 70

Vegan agedashi tofu 116
Veggie cannelloni 124
Veggie katsu rice bowl 78
Vietnamese turmeric fish 64

WALNUTS
Coffee & walnut angel cake 172
Warm courgette pasta salad 125

WRAPS
Breakfast tacos with
avocado & lime sauce 142
Pea & Parma ham quiche 94
Speedy veggie pizza 74
Steak & pepper quesadillas 112
Turkey, apple & smoked
Cheddar wraps 88

YOGURT
Banana, berry & chocolate
cereal pots 110
Chia & coconut Bircher
muesli with blueberry compote 110
Frozen chocolate
& raspberry bark 137
Frozen yogurt-coated blueberries 136
Peach & almond baked oats 111
Seed crackers with artichoke dip 134
Tropical fruit Charlotte 205

Zesty asparagus, beans & peas 150

SmartPoints index

Green

1 SmartPoint
Frozen chocolate & raspberry bark	137
Frozen yogurt-coated blueberries	136
Zesty asparagus, beans & peas	150

2 SmartPoints
Courgette bites with feta dip	178
Creamed greens	150
Pumpkin & chia seed bites	102
Spicy roasted chickpeas	132
Spring onion & bacon mini muffins	105

3 SmartPoints
Balsamic beetroot & ricotta toasts	179
Beetroot & blueberry smoothie	86
Carrot cake flapjacks	100
Celeriac & smoked haddock gratin	30
Chicken tom yum soup	60
Choc-chip flapjack bites	136
Herbed crushed new potatoes	151
Hot & spicy pulse pot	104
PBJ granola cups	102
Peanut butter & banana ice-cream sandwiches	204
Sesame chicken salad	91
Sweet potato & chickpea rolls	178

4 SmartPoints
Apple pie cookies	104
Baked oat waffles	24
Banana, berry & chocolate cereal pots	110
Banana mocha frappe	86
Barbecued miso aubergines	184
Cauliflower 'wings' with chickpea dip	180
Chia & coconut Bircher muesli with blueberry compote	110
Roasted cauliflower, ham & mustard frittata	98
Sesame prawns with sriracha	176
Spanish chicken & butter bean bravas	122

5 SmartPoints
Cranberry & thyme gin cocktail	176
'Creamy' vegetable pasanda	76
Raspberry & coconut soufflés	200
Raspberry blondies	103
Seed crackers with artichoke dip	134
Vegan agedashi tofu	116

6 SmartPoints
Baked rice pudding	46
Bloody Mary omelette	26
Chilli crab pasta	158
Chocolate financiers	172

Fig & mascarpone roulade	202
Frying pan peach crumble	48
Herb-crusted side of salmon	192
Homemade granola	84
Italian-style pesto salad	90
Portobello mushroom 'pizza'	80
Pulled chicken bao buns	156
Roasted apples with cinder toffee	48
Roasted strawberry & almond overnight oats	87
Scrambled eggs with mushrooms & smoked trout	108
Shawarma chicken with fattoush salad	56
Smoked salmon sharing rösti	143
Smoky salmon & chorizo skewers	184
Spring chicken traybake	114
Tamarind-glazed salmon with crunchy naked slaw	118
Tapenade tuna salad	120
Turkey, apple & smoked Cheddar wraps	88
Warm courgette pasta salad	125

7 SmartPoints
Apple & blackberry sponge puddings	49
Apricot tarte tatin	170
Aubergine & lentil puttanesca with Parma-wrapped cod	164
Breakfast rolls	27
Caramelised banana porridge	26
Cheese & gherkin toastie	28
Harissa steak salad	126
Homemade beans on toast	140
Honey & soy-glazed ham	196
Hot smoked salmon Caesar salad	90
Indonesian-style coconut prawns with cauliflower rice	58
Pork cassoulet	38
Pulled mushroom chilli with baked potato mash	40
Steak & pepper quesadillas	112
Tropical fruit Charlotte	205
Turkey meatball sliders	154
Veggie katsu rice bowl	78

8 SmartPoints
Crispy gnocchi with ham hock & shredded greens	162
Coffee & walnut angel cake	172
Lemon mousse with ginger crumb	204
Pasta with anchovies & capers	124
Peach & almond baked oats	111
Roasted lamb with salsa verde beans	148
Roast pork with onion gravy	146
Speedy veggie pizza	74

Sticky pudding with apple crisps	168
Sticky spiced chicken & butternut squash traybake	128
Veggie cannelloni	124
Vietnamese turmeric fish	64

9 SmartPoints
Breakfast tacos with avocado & lime sauce	142
Cauliflower wellington	194
French onion hotdogs	54
Hotdog hash	142
Korean veggie stir-fry with crispy rice	80
Lettuce cup beef tacos with jalapeño sauce	62
Melt-in-the-middle burgers	52
Oven-baked pumpkin & porcini risotto	44
Pea & Parma ham quiche	94
Pesto chicken pasta salad	96
Pumpkin pie pancakes	144
Spiced turkey mujadarra	130
Sriracha pork chops with celeriac & butter bean mash	166
Teriyaki cod with soba noodle salad	72

10 SmartPoints
Cheese & onion pie with minted greens	152
Chocolate celebration cake	198
Greek-style pork souvlaki with tomato rice salad	66
Griddled rump steak with chips & mustard 'mayo'	182
Keralan chicken curry soup	31
Kung pao turkey stir-fry	54
Scallop & leek risotto	190
Soy salmon with sweet & sour aubergines	160
Spring vegetable spanakopita	92
Sweet chilli fish & chips traybake	68
Turkey & leek bake	30
Turkish steak pittas	186

11 SmartPoints
Balsamic-glazed sausages with roasted garlic mash	34
Beef bulgogi noodle stir-fry	55
Beer-glazed chicken skewers with succotash	188
Chicken & mushroom stroganoff	32
Fish pie potato skins	36
Turkish-style lamb skewers with couscous	70

12 SmartPoints
Roast chicken dinner traybake	42

Blue

0 SmartPoints
Spanish chicken & butter bean bravas — 122
Spicy roasted chickpeas — 132

1 SmartPoint
Bloody Mary omelette — 26
Frozen chocolate & raspberry bark — 137
Frozen yogurt-coated blueberries — 136
Roasted cauliflower, ham & mustard frittata — 98
Scrambled eggs with mushrooms & smoked trout — 108
Tamarind-glazed salmon with crunchy naked slaw — 118
Zesty asparagus, beans & peas — 150

2 SmartPoints
Cauliflower 'wings' with chickpea dip — 180
Celeriac & smoked haddock gratin — 30
Chicken tom yum soup — 60
Courgette bites with feta dip — 178
Creamed greens — 150
Herb-crusted side of salmon — 192
Hot & spicy pulse pot — 104
Pumpkin & chia seed bites — 102
Sesame chicken salad — 91
Spring onion & bacon mini muffins — 105
Vegan agedashi tofu — 116

3 SmartPoints
Apple pie cookies — 104
Balsamic beetroot & ricotta toasts — 179
Banana, berry & chocolate cereal pots — 110
Beetroot & blueberry smoothie — 86
Carrot cake flapjacks — 100
Choc-chip flapjack bites — 136
Herbed crushed new potatoes — 151
PBJ granola cups — 102
Peanut butter & banana ice-cream sandwiches — 204
Sesame prawns with sriracha — 176
Smoky salmon & chorizo skewers — 184
Sweet potato & chickpea rolls — 178

4 SmartPoints
Baked oat waffles — 24
Banana mocha frappe — 86
Barbecued miso aubergines — 184
Chia & coconut Bircher muesli with blueberry compote — 110
Homemade beans on toast — 140
Raspberry blondies — 103
Smoked salmon sharing rösti — 143

Spring chicken traybake — 114
Tapenade tuna salad — 120

5 SmartPoints
Breakfast rolls — 27
Breakfast tacos with avocado & lime sauce — 142
Cranberry & thyme gin cocktail — 176
'Creamy' vegetable pasanda — 76
Hot smoked salmon Caesar salad — 90
Pea & Parma ham quiche — 94
Peach & almond baked oats — 111
Pork cassoulet — 38
Pulled chicken bao buns — 156
Raspberry & coconut soufflés — 200
Seed crackers with artichoke dip — 134
Shawarma chicken with fattoush salad — 56
Soy salmon with sweet & sour aubergines — 160

6 SmartPoints
Apple & blackberry sponge puddings — 49
Aubergine & lentil puttanesca with Parma-wrapped cod — 164
Baked rice pudding — 46
Balsamic-glazed sausages with roasted garlic mash — 34
Beer-glazed chicken skewers with succotash — 188
Chilli crab pasta — 158
Chocolate financiers — 172
Fig & mascarpone roulade — 202
Frying pan peach crumble — 48
Homemade granola — 84
Italian-style pesto salad — 90
Portobello mushroom 'pizza' — 80
Pulled mushroom chilli with baked potato mash — 40
Roasted apples with cinder toffee — 48
Roasted strawberry & almond overnight oats — 87
Roasted lamb with salsa verde beans — 148
Sticky spiced chicken & butternut squash traybake — 128
Tropical fruit Charlotte — 205
Turkey, apple & smoked Cheddar wraps — 88
Turkey meatball sliders — 154
Veggie cannelloni — 124
Warm courgette pasta salad — 125

7 SmartPoints
Apricot tarte tatin — 170
Caramelised banana porridge — 26
Cheese & gherkin toastie — 28
Harissa steak salad — 126

Honey & soy-glazed ham — 196
Hotdog hash — 142
Indonesian-style coconut prawns with cauliflower rice — 58
Lemon mousse with ginger crumb — 204
Lettuce cup beef tacos with jalapeño sauce — 62
Pesto chicken pasta salad — 96
Steak & pepper quesadillas — 112
Sticky pudding with apple crisps — 168
Teriyaki cod with soba noodle salad — 72
Veggie katsu rice bowl — 78
Vietnamese turmeric fish — 64

8 SmartPoints
Cheese & onion pie with minted greens — 152
Coffee & walnut angel cake — 172
Crispy gnocchi with ham hock & shredded greens — 162
Greek-style pork souvlaki with tomato rice salad — 66
Pasta with anchovies & capers — 124
Pumpkin pie pancakes — 144
Roast pork with onion gravy — 146
Speedy veggie pizza — 74
Spiced turkey mujadarra — 130
Spring vegetable spanakopita — 92
Sriracha pork chops with celeriac & butter bean mash — 166
Sweet chilli fish & chips traybake — 68

9 SmartPoints
Cauliflower wellington — 194
Fish pie potato skins — 36
French onion hotdogs — 54
Griddled rump steak with chips & mustard 'mayo' — 182
Keralan chicken curry soup — 31
Korean veggie stir-fry with crispy rice — 80
Kung pao turkey stir-fry — 54
Melt-in-the-middle burgers — 52
Oven-baked pumpkin & porcini risotto — 44
Turkey & leek bake — 30
Turkish steak pittas — 186

10 SmartPoints
Chicken & mushroom stroganoff — 32
Chocolate celebration cake — 198
Scallop & leek risotto — 190

11 SmartPoints
Beef bulgogi noodle stir-fry — 55
Roast chicken dinner traybake — 42
Turkish-style lamb skewers with couscous — 70

SmartPoints index

Purple

0 SmartPoints
Herbed crushed new potatoes 151
Spanish chicken & butter
bean bravas 122
Spicy roasted chickpeas 132
Spring chicken traybake 114

1 SmartPoint
Baked oat waffles 24
Bloody Mary omelette 26
Frozen chocolate &
raspberry bark 137
Frozen yogurt-coated
blueberries 136
Pulled mushroom chilli
with baked potato mash 40
Pumpkin & chia seed bites 102
Roasted cauliflower, ham
& mustard frittata 98
Scrambled eggs with
mushrooms & smoked trout 108
Tamarind-glazed salmon
with crunchy naked slaw 118
Zesty asparagus, beans & peas 150

2 SmartPoints
Carrot cake flapjacks 100
Cauliflower 'wings' with
chickpea dip 180
Celeriac & smoked
haddock gratin 30
Chia & coconut Bircher muesli
with blueberry compote 110
Chicken tom yum soup 60
Choc-chip flapjack bites 136
Courgette bites with feta dip 178
Creamed greens 150
Herb-crusted side of salmon 192
Hot & spicy pulse pot 104
Pasta with anchovies & capers 124
PBJ granola cups 102
Peach & almond baked oats 111
Sesame chicken salad 91
Spring onion & bacon
mini muffins 105
Smoked salmon sharing rösti 143
Sweet potato & chickpea rolls 178
Vegan agedashi tofu 116

3 SmartPoints
Apple pie cookies 104
Balsamic beetroot &
ricotta toasts 179
Banana, berry & chocolate
cereal pots 110
Beetroot & blueberry smoothie 86
Caramelised banana porridge 26
Peanut butter & banana
ice-cream sandwiches 204
Roasted strawberry & almond
overnight oats 87

Sesame prawns with sriracha 176
Smoky salmon & chorizo
skewers 184
Sticky spiced chicken
& butternut squash traybake 128
Sweet chilli fish &
chips traybake 68

4 SmartPoints
Banana mocha frappe 86
Barbecued miso aubergines 184
Chicken & mushroom stroganoff 32
Fish pie potato skins 36
Harissa steak salad 126
Homemade beans on toast 140
Homemade granola 84
Hotdog hash 142
Raspberry blondies 103
Spiced turkey mujadarra 130
Tapenade tuna salad 120
Teriyaki cod with soba
noodle salad 72
Warm courgette pasta salad 125

5 SmartPoints
Breakfast rolls 27
Breakfast tacos with
avocado & lime sauce 142
Cranberry & thyme gin cocktail 176
'Creamy' vegetable pasanda 76
Frying pan peach crumble 48
Griddled rump steak with chips
& mustard 'mayo' 182
Hot smoked salmon
Caesar salad 90
Pea & Parma ham quiche 94
Pork cassoulet 38
Pulled chicken bao buns 156
Raspberry & coconut soufflés 200
Roast pork with onion gravy 146
Seed crackers with
artichoke dip 134
Shawarma chicken with
fattoush salad 56
Soy salmon with sweet
& sour aubergines 160

6 SmartPoints
Apple & blackberry sponge
puddings 49
Aubergine & lentil puttanesca
with Parma-wrapped cod 164
Baked rice pudding 46
Balsamic-glazed sausages
with roasted garlic mash 34
Beer-glazed chicken skewers
with succotash 188
Chilli crab pasta 158
Chocolate financiers 172
Fig & mascarpone roulade 202
Italian-style pesto salad 90

Portobello mushroom 'pizza' 80
Roasted apples
with cinder toffee 48
Roasted lamb with salsa
verde beans 148
Tropical fruit Charlotte 205
Turkey, apple & smoked
Cheddar wraps 88
Turkey meatball sliders 154
Veggie cannelloni 124

7 SmartPoints
Apricot tarte tatin 170
Beef bulgogi noodle stir-fry 55
Cheese & gherkin toastie 28
Cheese & onion pie with
minted greens 152
Honey & soy-glazed ham 196
Indonesian-style coconut
prawns with cauliflower rice 58
Keralan chicken curry soup 31
Lemon mousse with
ginger crumb 204
Lettuce cup beef tacos with
jalapeño sauce 62
Pesto chicken pasta salad 96
Roast chicken dinner traybake 42
Steak & pepper quesadillas 112
Sticky pudding with
apple crisps 168
Veggie katsu rice bowl 78
Vietnamese turmeric fish 64

8 SmartPoints
Crispy gnocchi with ham
hock & shredded greens 162
Coffee & walnut angel cake 172
Greek-style pork souvlaki with
tomato rice salad 66
Pumpkin pie pancakes 144
Speedy veggie pizza 74
Spring vegetable spanakopita 92
Sriracha pork chops with
celeriac & butter bean mash 166
Turkish-style lamb skewers
with couscous 70

9 SmartPoints
Cauliflower wellington 194
French onion hotdogs 54
Korean veggie stir-fry with
crispy rice 80
Kung pao turkey stir-fry 54
Melt-in-the-middle burgers 52
Oven-baked pumpkin
& porcini risotto 44
Turkey & leek bake 30
Turkish steak pittas 186

10 SmartPoints
Chocolate celebration cake 198
Scallop & leek risotto 190